A Sense of
PLACE

TO KNOW   TO UNDERSTAND   TO PARTICIPATE
THE CANADIAN HERITAGE IS YOUR HERITAGE

**ALBERTA HERITAGE
LEARNING RESOURCES
PROJECT**

A Project of Alberta Education
Funded
By
The Alberta Heritage Savings Trust Fund
and
Dedicated to the Students
of Alberta
by the
Government of Alberta
1979

Grateful acknowledgment is extended
to those who assisted in the development
of the Alberta Heritage anthologies

Members of the Selection Committee

Theresa Ford / *Edmonton Catholic School District*
Michael Allen / *Calgary Catholic School District*
Tom Gee / *Alberta Education*
Marg Iveson / *Edmonton Public School District*
Gloria Limin / *Calgary Public School District*
Lorne MacRae / *Calgary Public School District*
Maureen Ross / *Edmonton Catholic School District*

Western Canadian Literature
for Youth

A Sense of
PLACE

Theresa M. Ford
Managing Editor

Alberta Education
Edmonton

Alberta Education
Devonian Building
11160 Jasper Avenue
Edmonton, Alberta
T5K 0L2

ISBN 0-920794-02-5

Project Director / Dr. Kenneth Nixon
Design / David Shaw & Associates Ltd.
Publishing Consultants / Hurtig Publishers, Edmonton
Illustration / Vlasta van Kampen
Typesetting / The Albertan, Calgary
Printing / Lawson Graphics Western Ltd., Calgary
Binding / Economy Bookbinding Company Ltd., Calgary

To the Reader

Every one of us, as a human being, is a unique individual, different in diverse ways from every other human being.

This statement is an over-simplification of a very complex fact of life. If all of us can claim our own particular identities, it is because we have been affected by a wide variety of people, places, and experiences. Of prime importance are our families — immediate and extended — our friends, our traditions, and our physical surroundings. Without them, we would not be *who* we are, *what* we are or, indeed, *where* we are.

A Sense of Place examines these relationships and experiences through a variety of actual and fictional characters. We sincerely hope that the reading of these selections will enable you to come to a realization of *your* sense of place within your family, your society, and your world.

Contents

Generations

Traditions

Where Is My Home?

Friendships

The Outlaw

Sinclair Ross

She was beautiful but dangerous. She had thrown one man and killed him, thrown another and broken his collar bone, and my parents, as if they knew what the sight of her idle in her stall was doing to me, never let a day go by without giving lurid details, everything from splints and stitches to the undertaker, of the painful and untimely end in store for me should I ever take it into my fool young head to try to ride her.

"I've got troubles enough without having you laid up with broken bones and doctor bills. She's a sly one, mind no good's ever come of her."

"Besides, you're only turned thirteen, and a grown man, a regular cowboy at that, would think twice before tackling her. Another year and then we'll see. You'll both be that much older. In the meantime nobody expects it of you."

In the meantime, though, she was a captive, pining her heart away. Week after week she stamped and pawed, nosed the hay out of her manger contemptuously, flung up her head and poured out wild, despairing neighs into the prairie winds and blizzards streaming past. It was mostly, of course, for my benefit. She had sized me up, evidently, as soft-hearted as well as faint-hearted, and decided there was just a chance that I might weaken and go riding. Her neighs, just as she intended they should, tormented and shamed me.

She was a good horse, but a reprobate. That was how we came to own her. At the auction sale where she was put up, her reputation as a killer spread among the crowd, and my father got her cheap. He was such a practical, level-headed man, and she was so obviously a poor investment, that I suspect it was because of me he bought her. As I stood at his side in the front row of the crowd and watched them lead her out, poised, dramatic, radiant, some of the sudden desire that overwhelmed me must have leaped from my face and melted him.

"Anyway, she's a bargain," he defended himself that evening at the supper table. "I can always sell her and at least get back what I paid. But first I want to see what a taste of good hard work will do."

He tried it. His intention was to work her on the land a month or two, just till she was tamed down to make an all-round, serviceable saddle horse, but after a painful week of half-days on the plow he let her keep her stall. She was too hard on his nerves, he said, straining ahead and pulling twice her share. She was too hard on his self-respect, actually, the slender limbs, the imperious head.

For she was a very lovely reprobate. Twenty years of struggle with the land had made him a determined, often hard man, but he couldn't bring himself to break her spirit with the plow.

She was one horse, and she was all horses: Thundering battle charges, fleet Arabians, untamed mustangs — sitting beside her on her manger I knew and rode them all. There was history in her shapely head and burning eyes. I charged with her at Balaklava, Waterloo, scoured the deserts of Africa and the steppes of the Ukraine. Conquest and carnage, trumpets and glory — she understood, and carried me triumphantly.

To approach her was to be enlarged, transported. She was coal-black, gleaming, queenly. Her mane had a ripple and her neck an arch. And somehow, softly and mysteriously, she was always burning. The reflection on her glossy hide, whether of winter sunshine or yellow lantern light, seemed the glow of some fierce, secret passion. There were moments when I felt the whole stable charged with her, as if she were the priestess of her kind, in communion with her deity.

For all that, though, she was a very dangerous horse, and dutifully my parents kept warning me. Facts didn't lie, they pointed out. A record was a record.

Isabel did her utmost to convince me that the record was a slander. With nuzzling, velvet lips she coaxed and pleaded, whispered that the delights of fantasy and dream were but as shadows beside the exhilarations of reality. Only try reality — slip her bridle on. Only be reasonable — ask myself what she would gain by throwing me. After all, I was turned thirteen. It wasn't as if I were a *small* boy.

And then, temptress, she bore me off to the mountain top of my vanity, and with all the world spread out before my gaze, talked guilefully of prestige and acclaim.

Over there, three miles away, was the school house. What a sensation to come galloping up on her, the notorious outlaw, instead of jogging along as usual on bandy-legged old Pete. What a surprise for Millie Dickson whose efforts to be loyal to me were always defeated by my lack of nerve and daring. For it was true: On the playground I had only a fair rating. I was butterfingers when it came to ball, and once in a fight I had cravenly turned tail and run. How sweet to wipe out all the ignominy of my past, to be deferred to by the older boys, to bask in Millie's smiles of favour.

And over there, seven miles away, the cupolas of its grain elevators just visible on the horizon, was town. Where fairs were sometimes held, and races run. On such a horse I naturally would win, and for all I knew the prize might be a hundred dollars. Well, then — supposing I could treat Millie to ice-cream *and* a movie!

Here Isabel would pause a moment, contemptuous of one so craven, then whinney shrill in challenge to some other rider, with heart and spirit equal to her own. There was no one, of course, to hear the challenge, but still it always troubled me. Johnny Olsen, for instance, the show-off Swede who had punched my nose and made me run — supposing he should come along and say, "I'll ride her for you — I'm not scared!" What kind of figure then would I cut? What would Millie Dickson say?

Isabel's motives, in all this, were two. The first was a natural, purely equine desire to escape from her stall and stretch her legs. The second, equally strong, was a perverse, purely feminine itch to bend me to her will.

For it was a will as imperious as her head. Her pride was at stake; I had to be reduced. With the first coaxing nuzzle of her lips she had committed herself to the struggle, and that as a male I was still at such a rudimentary stage made it doubly imperative that she emerge the victor. Defeat by a man would have been defeat, bitter but endurable. Defeat by a boy, on the other hand, would have been sheer humiliation.

On account of the roads and weather school was closed for two months after Christmas, and as the winter wore on it became increasingly difficult to resist her. A good deal of the time my father was away with wheat to town, and it was three miles to the nearest neighbour where there was another boy. I had chores, books, and the toolshed to keep me busy, but still there were long hours of idleness. Hungry for companionship, it was only natural that I should turn to Isabel. There were always her tail and mane to comb when we wearied of each other conversationally.

My association with her, of course, was virtual disobedience. I knew that she was charging me with desire, that eventually under its pressure I must burst like a blister, but still, despite conscience and good intentions, I lingered. Leaving her was always difficult, like leaving a fair or picnic, and going home to hunt the cows.

And then one clear sharp day, early in February, Millie Dickson and her mother drove over to spend the afternoon, and suddenly the temptation was too much for me.

They came early, country-fashion, so that Mrs. Dickson would have time for a long talk and tea, and be home again before nightfall. My father was away to town, and when they drove up in their bright red cutter I hurried out to take the horse. Mrs. Dickson was generous in her thanks, and even Millie smiled invitingly from beneath her frosted yellow curls. She had always liked me well enough. It was just that my behaviour at school made it difficult to be my champion.

I was shy when I returned to the house, but exceedingly happy. We all sat in the kitchen, not only because it was the largest, warmest room, but also because it gave my mother a chance to entertain her guest and at the same time whip up fresh biscuits and a cake in their honour. Mrs. Dickson asked so many friendly questions that I squirmed with pleasure till the varnish on my chair was fairly blistered. What could it mean but that at home Millie did champion me, that she suppressed the discreditable and spoke only of the best?

She and I talked, too. We leafed through old magazines, gossiped about school, speculated on the new teacher, and gradually established a sense of intimacy and good will that made me confident my past was all forgotten, my future rosy and secure. For an hour it was like that — socially the most gratifying hour I had ever spent — and then, as nearly always happened when my mother had visitors, the delinquencies and scandals of the community moved in, and the kitchen became a place unfit for innocent young ears.

There must have been a considerable number of these delinquencies. It was indeed a very upright, fine community, but it must have had its wayward side. Anyway, surveying my entire boyhood, I am sure I could count on the fingers of one hand the times I was *not* sent out to chop wood or look for eggs when my mother and her friends got started on the neighbours. Usually I had a fair idea from the thread of conversation who it was who had been up to what, but this time, absorbed in my relationship with Millie, I heard nothing till my mother tapped my shoulder.

"Come along," she said brightly, affecting concern for our appetites and health. "It's too fine a day for you and Millie to be sitting in the house. Run out and play in the fresh air, so you'll be ready for your tea."

But at thirteen you don't play with a girl. You can neither skin the cat with her up in the loft among the rafters, nor turn somersaults down a strawstack. I did suggest taking the .22 and going after rabbits, but the dear little bunnies were so sweet, she said, she couldn't bear to hurt them. Naturally, therefore, after a chilly and dispiriting turn or two around the barnyard, I took her in to visit Isabel.

Isabel rose to the occasion. She minced and pawed, strained at her halter shank to let us see how badly she wanted to be taken out, then nipped our sleeves to prove her gentle playfulness. And finally, to remind us that despite such intimacies she was by no means an ordinary horse, she lifted her head and trumpeted out one of her wild, dramatic neighs.

Millie was impressed. "That wonderful way she holds her head," she said. "just like a picture. If only you could ride her to school."

"Nobody rides her — anywhere," I replied curtly. "She's an outlaw." And then, as her mouth drooped in disappointment, "At least nobody's *supposed* to ride her."

She jumped for it. "You mean you do ride her? And she doesn't throw you?"

"Of course," I conceded modestly, "she's very easy to ride. Such speed — and smooth as a rocking chair. When you look down the ground's just like water running past. But she could throw me all right if she had a mind to."

Millie sighed. "I'd like so much though to *see* you ride her. Today — isn't it a good chance, with them in there talking and your father away to town?"

I hesitated, overcome by a feeling of fright and

commitment, and then Isabel too joined in. She begged and wheedled, looked so innocent, at the same time so hurt and disappointed that Millie exclaimed she felt like going for a ride herself. And that settled it. "Stand at the door and see no one's coming," I commanded. "I'll put her bridle on."

Isabel practically put it on herself. She gave a shrill excited whinny as I led her out, pranced like a circus pony, pushed me along still faster with her nose. "No," I answered Millie shortly, "I don't use the saddle. You don't get sore, she rides so easy. And in case she turns mean I don't get tangled in the stirrups."

With a flutter in her voice Millie said, "Do you really think you should?" and in response I steeled myself, nonchalantly turned up the collar of my sheepskin. "At the rate she goes," I explained, "the wind cuts through you like a knife."

To myself I reflected, "There's plenty of snow. At the worst it will only be a spill. "

Isabel stood quite still till I was mounted. She even stood still a moment longer, letting me gather myself, take a firm grip of the reins, crouch low in readiness. Then with a plunge, a spasm of muscles, she was off. And it was true: The wind cut sharp and bitter like a knife, the snow slipped past like water. Only in her motion there was a difference. She was like a rocket, not a rocking chair.

It was nearly a mile, though, before I began properly to understand what was happening. Isabel the outlaw — the horse that had killed a man, that people talked about for fifty miles — here was I, just turned thirteen, and riding her. And an immense pride filled me. Cold as I was I pushed my sheepskin collar down and straightened recklessly to feel the rush of wind. I needed it that way, a counteracting sting of cold to steady the exhilaration.

We had gone another mile before I remembered Millie, and at once, as if sensitive to my concern, Isabel drew up short for breath. She didn't drop to a trot or walk as an ordinary horse would have done, but instead, with the clean grace and precision of a bird alighting on a branch, came smoothly to a halt. And for a moment or two, before starting home again, she rested. The prairie spread before us cold and sparkling in the winter sunlight, and poised and motionless, ears pricked forwards, nostrils faintly quivering, she breathed in rapturously its loping miles of freedom.

And I too, responsive to her bidding, was aware as never before of its austere, unrelenting beauty. There were the white fields and the blue, metallic sky; the little splashes here and there of yellow strawstack, luminous and clear as drops of gum on fresh pine lumber; the scattered farmsteads brave and wistful in their isolation; the gleam of sun and snow. I wanted none of it, but she insisted. Thirteen years old and riding an outlaw — naturally I wanted only that. I wanted to indulge shamelessly my vanity, to drink the daring and success of my exploit in full-strength draughts, but Isabel, like a conscientious teacher at a fair, dragging you off to see instructive things, insisted on the landscape.

Look, she said firmly, while it's here before you, so that to the last detail it will remain clear. For you, too, some day there may be stalls and halters, and it will be a good memory.

But only for a moment or two, and then we were off again. She went even faster going home. She disdained and rebelled against her stall, but the way she whipped the wind around my ears you would have thought she had suddenly conceived a great affection for it. It was a strong wind, fiercely cold. There was a sharp sting in my ears for a minute, then sudden warmth and ease. I knew they were frozen, but there wasn't time to worry. I worked my collar up, crouched low again. Her mane blew back and lashed my face. Before the steady blast of wind my forehead felt as if the bone were wearing thin. But I didn't mind. I was riding her and holding on. I felt fearless, proud, mature. All the shame and misgivings of the past were over. I was now both her master and my own.

And then she was fifteen or twenty feet away, demurely watching me, and 1 was picking myself up and spitting snow.

She had done it with the utmost skill, right head first into a snowdrift, where I wouldn't hurt myself, less than a quarter of a mile from home.

And not even to toss her head and gallop off so that Millie would think she had done it in a fit of fright or meanness. Just to stand there, a picture of puzzled innocence, blandly transferring all the blame on me. What was wrong? Just when we were getting on so splendidly — why on earth had I deserted her?

For in her own way, despite her record, Isabel was something of a moralist. She took a firm stand against pride that wasn't justified. She considered my use of the word "master" insufferably presumptuous. Being able to ride an outlaw was not the same thing at all as being accorded the privilege of riding one, and for the good of my soul, it was high time I appreciated the distinction.

She stood still, sniffing in my direction, until I had almost reached her, then gave a disdainful snort and trotted pertly home. At the stable door she was waiting for me. I approached limping — not because I was hurt, but because with Millie standing back a little distance, goggle-eyed, I felt it looked better, made my tumble less an occasion for laughter — and as if believing me Isabel thrust her nose out, all condolence, and felt me tenderly where I was pretending it was sore. From the bottom of her heart she hoped I wouldn't be so unfortunate another time. So far as she was concerned, however, she could make no promises. There had been one fall, she explained to Millie, and there might easily be another. The future was entirely up to me. She couldn't be responsible for my horsemanship.

"Your ears are frozen," Millie changed the subject. "And your mother knows everything — she's going to let your father handle you."

I looked at her accusingly, but in a smug, self-righteous

tone she explained, "She called you twice, and then came out to see why you didn't answer. Just in time to see it happen. I'll rub your ears with snow if you like before we go in for tea."

It was a good tea, but I didn't eat much. My ears were not only swelling badly and turning purple; they were also starting to drip. My mother pinned a wash cloth to each shoulder, then sprinkled on talcum powder. She said nothing, but was ominously white-lipped and calm — saving herself up, I didn't doubt, until we were alone. I was in misery to escape upstairs to a mirror, but she insisted, probably as a kind of punishment, that I stay and finish my tea. Millie, I noticed, didn't eat much either, and kept her eyes turned fastidiously away.

When finally Mrs. Dickson and Millie were gone — and as an additional humiliation, I wasn't allowed out to bring round their horse — my mother replaced the wash cloths with towels. Still silent, still white-lipped, and since there was no need, now that we were alone, for her to keep on saving herself up, it struck me that perhaps the condition of my ears was really serious.

"They're smarting bad — and throbbing," I said hopefully. "It must have been colder than I thought."

"It must have been," she agreed. "Go up to your room now out of my way till suppertime. I'd better talk to your father before he sees you anyway."

I knew then that she was as afraid of what was in store for me as I was. Her expression remained stern, but there was a softness in her voice, a note of anxiety. It was a good sign, but it was also a bad one. It meant that she expected my father's anger to be explosive and extreme.

Upstairs, swollen and tender as they were, I gave my ears a brisk rubbing. They were already dripping and unsightly. A little worse, a darker, a more alarming purple, and they might get me out of a hiding.

While waiting I also rehearsed a number of entrances, a number of defences, but at the last minute abandoned all of them. The heat in my ears as I went downstairs was spreading like a prairie fire, and when I entered the kitchen there was such a blaze of it across my eyes that I could make out my father only as a vague, menacing form. A desperate resolve seized me; should he so much as threaten the razor strap I would ride away on Isabel and be lost to them forever.

But instead of pouncing he looked me over critically a minute, then hitched in his chair to the table and began buttering a piece of bread. "Some bronco buster," he said at last, in a weary, disillusioned voice. "All you need now is a ten-gallon."

"I didn't have the saddle — and she stopped short and shied." My voice climbed defensively. In dramatization of the suddenness of the stop I drove a clenched fist into an open palm. "I had been sticking on all right though — for four miles or more."

"Anyway," he said resignedly, "you've got yourself a pretty pair of ears."

I raised a quick, self-conscious hand to touch them, and my mother assured me, "They're still there all right — don't worry. They made a hit with Millie too, judging by the look on her face. I think she'll be seeing them tonight in her sleep."

"But the mare," my father interrupted in a man-to-man tone of voice, abruptly cold-shouldering my mother, "how did you find her? Mean as she's supposed to be?"

"Not mean at all. Even when I was getting on — she stood and let me."

"Next time, just the same, you'd better play safe and use a snaffle. I'll hunt one up for you. It won't hurt her so long as she behaves."

"The next time!" my mother cried. "Talking about the next time when you ought to be taking down his breeches. She's not fit horse for a boy. If nobody'll buy her you ought to give her away, before she breaks somebody else's neck."

She went on a long time like that, but I didn't pay much

attention. Pride — that was what it amounted to — pride even greater than mine had been before I landed in the snowdrift. It sent me soaring a minute, took my breath away, but it also brought a little shiver of embarrassment and shame. How long, then, had I kept them waiting? How many times in the past few months had they looked at me and despaired?

"One thing," my mother declared with finality, "you're not riding her to school. The things I'd be thinking and seeing all day — I just couldn't stand it."

"You hear," my father agreed. "I'll not have you carrying on with a lot of young fools crazy as yourself — being a good fellow, like as not, and letting them all ride her."

I was about to protest — as if any of them dared or could ride Isabel — but instead, remembering in time, went on docilely with my supper. Outwardly impassive, I was sky-high within. Just as Isabel herself had always said, what a sensation to ride foaming up to school at a breakneck, hair-raising gallop. In the past I had indulged the prospect sparingly. Indeed, with so many threats and warnings in my ears, it had never been a prospect at all, but only a fantasy, something to be thought about wishfully, like blacking both Johnny Olsen's eyes at once, or having five dollars to spend. Now, though, everything was going to be different. Now, in their peculiar parental idiom, they had just given their permission, and Isabel and the future were all mine. Isabel *and* Millie Dickson. In accompaniment to a fervent resolve to be worthy of them both, my ears throbbed happily.

So Young, So Brave
Clive Lytle

As she opened the door, Janet was greeted by the warm rich aroma of pie, hot from the oven. "I'm home, Mom," she called from the wide old hall, removing her coat. Janet stood for a moment, lost in thought, a rather tall, dark girl — pretty, with her dark, softly waved hair gently outlining her face. Finally, her reverie ended, she entered the kitchen.

"Busy at the office today, dear?" asked Mrs. Masters, as Janet kissed her lightly on the forehead.

"No, Mom; and Mom — I have to hurry. I have a date in an hour." Her mother turned from the stove.

"With Dan?"

"No, Mom," replied Janet. "His name is David — David Simpson," and then shyly, "He's very nice!" The sound of the front door opening interrupted their conversation. John Masters entered, tall and graying.

"Hello dear, steak for supper?" Janet kissed her father as she left the kitchen.

"Yes, John, steak; and you can sit down, it's ready," said Mrs. Masters. "Janet's going out with some young man she's just met — David Simmons, or something like that. I hope he's nice like Dan."

"I'm sure he will be, Martha," replied her husband, sitting down. "Our daughter's a good, sensible girl."

Later, as both sat reading over their coffee, Janet having gone upstairs to get her coat, the doorbell rang.

"I'll get it, Martha," said her husband. "It will probably be Janet's young man." He opened the door and his face froze.

After an awkward silence, the young man said: "I'm David Simpson: I'm here for Janet."

"Come in," said Mr. Masters, his voice faltering. At that moment, Janet came quickly down the stairs, then stopped.

"Hello, David," her voice was soft. "Dad, this is David Simpson; David — my father." David held out his hand.

"I'm pleased to meet you, sir." Janet's father hesitated, then shook the outstretched hand.

"We'll have to run, Dad, or we'll miss the beginning of the show." said Janet hurriedly. "Bye — bye, Mom."

"Good-bye, sir," said David quietly. Mr. Masters' good-bye was shaky as the two left.

"Martha, you saw him; what shall we do?" His wife's face was pale and drawn and she did not speak.

It was midnight when the car's lights shone in the window as it turned into the driveway. Neither of Janet's parents, who sat stiffly in the living-room, spoke. A few minutes later the door opened.

"Hello folks," said Janet, entering the room.

"Janet, sit down; your mother and I have something to say to you." Her father's voice was strained and unreal as he spoke.

"It's about David, isn't it?" she replied quietly.

"Oh, Janet," her mother cried out, " How . . ."

"Just a moment, Martha," interrupted Mr. Masters. "Don't get yourself upset. Now, Janet, this Simpson is no doubt a very nice fellow, but he's not our kind. What would your friends think if they saw you with him? You could hardly expect them to welcome him. And you could never become — well serious. Don't you think. . . ."

Janet broke in, her voice low but firm:

"Dad, listen to me. I like David very much. In time I may love him; now, I don't know. I don't care what colour his skin is. He is a fine man and that is all that is important. If my friends won't accept him, then I don't want them for friends. I am going to continue going out with him, and there's nothing you or anybody else can do to stop me. Now I'm going to bed; I'm very tired. Good-night, Dad; good-night, Mother." As she finished speaking, Janet turned and without looking back, ascended the stairs. John Masters turned to his wife and spoke.

Far into the night the steady murmur of conversation continued, broken only by an occasional excited outburst.

The haze of morning was giving way to the rich glow of the rising sun when Janet, dressed for the office, came slowly down the stairs. Despite her efforts to the contrary, her thoughts dwelt on the previous evening's happenings. Entering the kitchen, she was greeted cheerily by her mother.

"Good morning, dear, breakfast's ready." As the three ate, a strained silence enveloped the table.

Finally Janet's father cleared his throat awkwardly and spoke. "Janet, if you are going out with David this evening, why don't you bring him home afterward? Your mother will have some of those special sandwiches of hers made and . . ." His voice died out slowly. Janet smiled warmly.

"Thanks, Dad, I'd love to. I'm sure you'll like David."

"I'm sure we will, dear," said her mother gently. "I'm very sure we will."

It was dusk. In the living room, John Masters read the evening paper; in the kitchen, his wife, Martha, stood ironing; while upstairs, Janet stood before her mirror applying make-up. The doorbell's shrill ring broke the silence of the house.

"Will you get it, Dad?" called down Janet. Her father rose, paused for a moment, then, squaring his shoulders, walked to the door.

"Good-evening, David," he said, as he opened the door. "Come in and sit down. Janet will be down in a moment." He ushered the young man into the living room. "Cigarette?" he asked.

"Thanks, Mr. Masters," replied the younger man taking one. Both men rose as Janet's mother entered the room.

"Oh, Martha," said her husband, "I'd like you to meet David Simpson. David this is my wife, Martha."

"I'm very glad to meet you, Mrs. Masters."

"How do you do, David. Janet will be . . . oh, here she is now." Janet was smiling as she came into the room.

"Hello, David. Have you met mother?"

"Yes, I have," he replied.

"Well, shall we leave," she said. "I'm all ready." Mr. Masters followed them to the door and opened it.

"Good-night, folks," said Janet. "We'll see you later."

"Have a nice time!" called Mr. Masters as they walked to the car. He reached out and took his wife's trembling brown hand in his. "They will too, Martha. It will be hard, but they are young and youth has great courage." Silently they watched the blonde young man help their daughter into the car, her brown arm resting on his white one. The car was started and soon passed out of sight. Slowly the door closed.

Burns Night
Norman Ward

"The police were in our neighbourhood last night," Uncle Bob said in some vexation. "They had to be called in to quell an outbreak of bagpipe playing."

"You have Scottish neighbours?"

"The street is overrun with them. And every Burns Day they run amok, wearing kilts and brandishing sporrans in all directions."

"You know I'm part Scots myself," I told him. "And while I do not participate in their annual revels, I feel the Scots are a racial minority we must learn to tolerate."

"You're not the fellow who sent me that Scottish calendar?" Uncle Bob eyed me keenly. I said I was innocent, and he proceeded to air a curious grievance.

"This calendar," he said, "has a separate page for each week, and on each page there's a pretty bit of Scotch — I mean Scottish — scenery, and a poem. The poetry is awful."

"In what way?"

"It doesn't make sense. It seems to be written in English and yet it isn't. For instance, this week's poem goes:

The lasses o' the Ferry
They busk braw.
The lasses o' the Elie,
They ding a'."

"Sounds nice."

"Yes, but what does it mean?"

"Have you asked your neighbours?"

"My neighbours!" he said disgustedly. "They tell me it's great stuff. But they can't translate it."

He chuckled. "I fooled them last night."

"Burns Night is hardly a fair night on which to fool a Scot."

"They weren't all at their best," he admitted, "but it didn't seem to impair their judgement of poetry. I asked them what this one meant:

Sae kirtle slithered clin awa',
Sae tripes gang a' tae glory.
He screct his bool awi' sae glaw,
And gimp next door tae borry."

"And what did they say?"

"They hadn't a clue. But they were unanimous in saying it was exceptionally fine. There was a brief scuffle about whether it had actually been written by Burns himself, and for a while it looked as if the police would have to be called back. But they all agreed it was wonderful."

A sudden thought struck me, and I asked him where he had found the poem.

He grinned. "I wrote it mysel'," he said.

Carpet of Roses
Mary-Jo Burles

It was in the '30s I worked for Fred Dirkson. Ten dollars a month and my board for a 12-hour day, and darned lucky to have a job at all. I was a big kid for 17, six feet in my socks — which were usually full of holes — so the work didn't bother me. What did bother me was the miserable $10 a month which dribbled into my pockets $1 and $2 at a time and went the same way.

By rights the Dirksons couldn't afford a hired man at all. They sure didn't have any crop the summer I was there. Even the milk cows kept themselves thin wandering around looking for grass. But Fred Dirkson had hurt his back bad that spring and his own gang of kids was too small to do anything except get in the way, so he had to have somebody.

It wasn't a bad place to work. I put in my full day everyday but Sunday, and then after I'd done the milking I had time to myself. And the grub was good — plain, but lots of it. Mostly potatoes and meat, with thick slices of homemade bread and butter and most likely a custard or milk pudding for dessert.

They treated me good too. I don't suppose Mrs. Dirkson was more than 15 years older than me but she treated me like one of her own kids, only in a grown up sort of way so that I couldn't be offended. There were enough kids too. The first morning I was there they came tumbling out into the kitchen like gophers popping out of a hole. I tried to count them but they were all tow headed with blue eyes and so close to a size that I kept getting confused on which ones I'd already counted.

She saw me looking and started to laugh. "Six," she said and laughed again. It was a big laugh and the sound of it filled the kitchen and echoed around until all of us were laughing, just because it was a good sound to hear and good to be alive.

They all laughed a lot though I never could see what they

had to be so happy about. And they sang too. She sang all the time while she worked kneading the bread, or scrubbing the worn board floor with hardly a fleck of paint left on it, or patching clothes that didn't have room for more patches. Even the baby who couldn't talk yet sang with the rest of them and they all had a good laugh at him, with him laughing harder than anybody.

Nobody had much money in those years, but I guess the Dirksons had less than anybody around. Even today when I see a flour sack I remember how she shook every last bit of flour out of the cloth into the big bin, and then unravelled the thread so she had a good piece of cloth maybe a yard square. Maybe they had some things in the house that weren't made out of flour sacks, but just offhand I can't think of any. Left as they were they made pillow slips, opened up they were dish towels, sewed together they were sheets and sometimes they were made into underwear for the kids. Dyed different colors and fancied up with a bit of embroidery cotton they made table cloths, curtains, bedspreads or shirts.

I would have been perfectly happy there except for the car. Lots of people who had bought cars in the '20s were selling them because they couldn't afford the gas to run them, so it was a good time to buy. And I wanted one so bad it was an ache inside me every waking minute. I knew just how much chance I had to buy one on $10 a month. Every time I did manage to put away a dollar something came up.

That's the way it was the night I got mad. Mr. Dirkson and the little kids were in bed, and we were sitting in the kitchen. She was embroidering a big fancy peacock on a flour sack which was going to be the middle part of a bedspread, and squinting a little bit because the coal oil lamp didn't throw a very strong light. She was humming a little snatch of a song under her breath. I was pretending to read but sitting thinking of myself driving down the road in a shiny green Model A and knowing that the $18 I had saved up was going to have to buy me underwear and pants for that winter, and a new coat and boots too.

"Oh what the heck," I said, getting up and dropping my book on the floor. "Always singing. What is there to sing about, anyhow? Flour sacks and runny-nosed kids, that's what," and I started out the door.

"Sit down, Jim," she said and her voice wasn't laughing.

"I'm sorry," I mumbled. "I shouldn't have said that. I was just mad at everything."

"Sit down," she said again. She didn't take her eyes off the peacock she was sewing, but I could see her fingers shaking a bit and her cheeks getting red.

I sat down. "I'm sorry," I said again, and I really was.

"Now," she said, "what's this all about?" She put down her sewing and I was even more ashamed of myself when I saw how red and cracked her hands were from the lye in the strong homemade soap she used. I felt like a big bawl baby whining over a car I wanted but didn't really need, when they were scraping along without necessities and not complaining.

"Oh, it's nothing," I muttered. "I guess I'm just tired." But the words came out in spite of me and pretty soon she knew all about the car; by the time I finished she was smiling.

"But you've got the dream," she broke in. "That's better than nothing at all, having the thought of it. And if you keep dreaming long enough and working too, you'll get it. You just see if I'm not right. Why, days when I'm tired and grumpy and the bread won't rise and the children squabble and nothing goes right, I think about the parlor I'm going to have someday and I feel better just for seeing it in my mind."

My surprise must have showed. I knew they didn't have much but I guess it hadn't really occurred to me that they wanted anything better. It was a small house, just two bedrooms. They had one, I shared the other with the boys, and the overflow slept in what should have been the parlor.

She got up to move the coffee pot onto the stove. "I'll have lace curtains at the window, and a green rug with red roses on the floor, and when the minister calls I'll say, 'Do come in, Reverend. No, don't sit in the kitchen. Come into the parlor where it's cool.'" And she poured my coffee with a flourish like I was Reverend Palmer sitting in the parlor with my feet on the red roses on the rug, and we both laughed.

I left soon after that, but I kept in touch with them and even went back for a couple of Christmases.

And she was right, too. Things went pretty good for me, and when cattle prices went sky high in '51 I had a nice little herd built up and was able to trade in the old car on a new one, though it didn't have much resemblance to the old Model A I'd had my heart set on nearly 20 years before.

So when the youngest girl wrote me the next fall that her mother was going into the hospital for an operation and that the doctors weren't very hopeful, I got a man to run the place for a couple of days and went down to visit. She looked pretty peaked sitting up in bed in one of those hospital gowns that don't seem made to fit anybody, but she could still smile.

I didn't stay very long, but when I told her about the new car she gave a little echo of the old hearty laugh and said, "I told you so." Then it was time to leave and I went out to the farm with Mr. Dirkson. The old house had perked up a lot. It's surprising what a difference a bit of paint can make to a place and there was a nice shiny linoleum on the floors and they even had electricity. Times had been pretty good for them too, though I guess nobody ever makes all the money they think they need.

As soon as I saw the parlor I remembered. The lace curtains were at the windows and there was a pretty good looking chesterfield but the green carpet wasn't on the floor. Instead there was a linoleum rug in a sort of brown color, but it had roses all through it so I knew she hadn't forgotten. "I thought you'd have had a carpet in here," I said casually, "the way you've got everything fancied up."

"We were going to get one last fall when we sold the beef,"

said Mr. Dirkson. "But it seemed like there were so many other things it just didn't stretch that far."

We went to milk then, but I made up my mind that the green carpet was going to be there when she came home. I didn't have any idea what the things cost but after supper I mentioned it to Mr. Dirkson. "I'd like to do it," I said. "Call it a coming home present for her if you like."

I think it was that that made him agree. We all knew there wasn't too much chance of her coming home, but if we could pretend ourselves that we were fixing it up for her, maybe it would make it come true. It helped us feel better.

I went back up to the city next day. "Wall to wall broadloom is what you want," said the clerk. "That's what everybody is getting now."

"Not me," I said. "I want a green rug with red roses in it and I don't care what it costs. If you haven't got one just say so and I'll find some place that has."

That perked him up pretty fast and he got busy and showed me one that was perfect. The price just about floored me, though. It would take a fat two-year-old steer to pay for it but I didn't care. I arranged to have the rug delivered and laid and then went back to my own place. Mr. Dirkson was going to tell her about it and I got a kick out of thinking how she was finally going to see her dream come true.

It was just three weeks later that she died without ever having gone home. Mr. Dirkson phoned me about the funeral arrangements so I got the same fellow to do my chores and went back. The funeral was held at the house and the minister stood in the parlor like she'd pretended. I hardly heard what he said for wishing she could have seen it before she died.

Then all of a sudden as the sunlight streamed through the window I realized it didn't matter. She'd seen it there all those years when things were tough, never getting faded or dirty or worn, but always fresh and bright like the dream she had in her heart. Maybe that's the best part after all, though I still think it was the best steer I ever spent.

Fog
Ethel Wilson

For seven days fog settled down upon Vancouver. It crept in from the ocean, advancing in its mysterious way in billowing banks which swallowed up the land. In the Bay and the Inlet and False Creek, agitated voices spoke to one another. Small tugs that were waylaid in the blankets of fog cried shrilly and sharply "Keep away! Keep away! I am here!" Fishing-boats lay inshore. Large freighters mooed continuously like monstrous cows. The foghorns at Point Atkinson and the Lions' Gate Bridge kept up their bellowings. Sometimes the fog quenched the sounds, sometimes the sounds were loud and near. If there had not been this continuous dense fog, all the piping and boo-hooing would have held a kind of beauty; but it signified danger and warning. People knew that when the fog lifted they would see great freighters looking disproportionately large riding at anchor in the Bay because passage through the Narrows into the harbour was not safe. Within the harbour, laden ships could not depart but remained lying fog-bound at great expense in the stream . . . booo . . . booo . . . they warned. "I am here! Keep away!" All the ships listened. The CPR boat from Victoria crashed into the dock. Gulls collided in the pathless air. Water traffic ceased and there was no movement anywhere offshore.

In the street, cars crawled slowly. Drivers peered. Pedestrians emerged and vanished like smoke. Up the draw of False Creek, fog packed thick on the bridges. Planes were grounded. People cancelled parties. Everyone arrived late for everything.

Mrs. Bylow was an old woman who lived in a small old house which was more cabin than cottage in an unpleasant part of Mount Pleasant. For the fifth day she sat beside her window looking into the fog and cracking her knuckles because she had nothing else to do. If she had owned a telephone she would have talked all day for pastime, repeating herself and driving the party line mad.

Mrs. Bylow frequently sat alone and lonely. Her diurnal occupations had narrowed down to sleeping, waking to still another day, getting up, making and swallowing small meals, belching a little, cleaning up (a little), hoping, going to the bathroom, going to the Chinaman's corner store, reading the paper (and thank God for that, especially the advertisements), becoming suddenly aware again of the noise of the radio (and thank God for that, too) and forgetting again.

This, and not much more, was her life as she waited for the great dustman and the ultimate box. So Mrs. Bylow's days and months slid and slid away while age — taking advantage of her solitariness, her long unemployment of vestigial brain, her unawareness of a world beyond herself, her absence of preparation for the grey years — closed down upon her like a vice, no, more like a fog. There had been a time about ten years ago when Mrs. Bylow, sitting on her small porch, beckoned to the little neighbour children who played on the sidewalk.

"Come," said Mrs. Bylow, smiling and nodding.

The children came, and they all went into the kitchen. There was Mrs. Bylow's batch of fresh cookies and the children ate, looking around them, rapacious. They ate and ran away and once or twice a child hovered and said "Thank you." Perhaps that was not the child who said "Thank you", but parents speaking through the child ("Say Thank you to Mrs. Bylow!") so the child said "Thank you" and Mrs. Bylow was pleased. Sometimes the children lingered around the little porch, not hungry, but happy, noisy and greedy. Then Mrs. Bylow rejoiced at the tokens of love and took the children into the kitchen. But perhaps she had only apples and the children did not care for apples. "Haven't you got any cookies?" asked a bold one, "we got lotsa apples at home."

"You come Tuesday," said Mrs. Bylow, nodding and smiling, but the children forgot.

So within Mrs. Bylow these small rainbows of life (children, cookies, laughing, and beckoning) faded, although two neighbours did sometimes stop on their way home and talk for a few minutes and thus light up her day. Miss Casey who worked at the People's Friendly Market and was a smart dresser with fine red hair and Mrs. Merkle who was the managing type and had eyes like marbles and was President of the Ladies' Bowling Club dropped in from time to time and told Mrs. Bylow all about the illnesses of the neighbours which Mrs. Bylow enjoyed very much and could think about later. Mrs. Merkle told her about Mr. Galloway's broken hip and Miss Casey told her about her mother's diabetes and how she managed her injections, also about the woman who worked in her department when she didn't need to work and how her kid had gone wrong and was in the Juvenile Court. Mrs. Bylow was regaled by everything depressing that her two friends could assemble because she enjoyed bad news which was displayed to her chiefly against the backdrop of her own experience and old age. All these ailments, recalling memories of her own (". . . well I remember my Uncle Ernest's . . ."), provided a drama, as did the neglect and irresponsibility of the young generations. Like an old sad avid stupid judge she sat, passing judgement without ill will. It is not hard to understand why Mrs. Merkle and Miss Casey, hastening past Mrs. Bylow's gate which swung on old hinges, often looked straight ahead, walking faster and thinking I *must* go in and see her tomorrow.

During long periods of bad weather, as now in this unconquerable fog, time was a deep pit for Mrs. Bylow. Her hip was not very good. She should have belonged to a church (to such base uses can the humble and glorious act of worship come) or a club, to which she would at least look forward. Gone were the simple impossible joys of going to town, wandering through the shops, fingering and comparing cloth, cotton, and silk. Gone was the joy of the running children. Life, which had been pinkish and bluish, was grey. And now this fog.

So it was that on the fifth day of fog, Mrs. Bylow sat beside her window in a sort of closed-up dry well of boredom, cracking her knuckles and looking into the relentless blank that pressed against her window panes and kept her from seeing any movement on the sidewalk. Mrs. Merkle and Miss Casey were as though they had never been. I'm not surprised they wouldn't drop in, thought Mrs. Bylow modestly and without rancour, it couldn't be expected, it'll be all they can do to get home; and she pictured Miss Casey, with her flaming hair, wearing her leopard coat, pushing through the fog home to her mother. Diabetes, thought Mrs. Bylow, and she was sorry for old Mrs. Casey. Her indulgence of sorrow spread to include Miss Casey hurrying home looking so smart. Not much in life for her now, is there really, she thought, rocking. Mrs. Bylow peered again. She was insulted by this everywhere fog, this preventing fog. She needed a cup of cocoa and she had no cocoa. She repeated aloud a useful phrase, "The fog is lifting"; but the fog was not lifting.

Mrs. Bylow creaked to her feet. She wrapped herself up well, took her walking stick, and went unsteadily down her three steps. Then, not at all afraid, she turned to the left and, in a silence of velvet, she moved slowly along beside the picket fence which would guide her to Wong Kee's store. At her own corner a suggestion of sickly glow in the air told her that the street lamps were lighted. She moved on, screwing up her eyes against the greyish, yellow fog that invaded eyes, nose, mouth. At last another pale high glimmer informed her that she was near Wong Kee's store and, gasping, leaning now and then against the outside wall of the store itself, she reached the door with the comfortable knowledge that, once inside, she would find light and warmth. She would ask Wong Kee for his chair or a box and would sit down and take her ease while the Chinaman went with shuffling steps to the shelf where he kept the tins of cocoa. Wong Kee was a charming old man with good cheek-bones and a sudden tired Oriental smile. After Mrs.

Merkle and Miss Casey he was Mrs. Bylow's third friend. She pushed the door open and waddled into where there was this desired light and warmth, puffing a little.

Something was happening inside the store, a small whirlwind and fury. Mrs. Bylow was roughly pushed by large rushing objects. She lost her balance and was thrown, no, hurled violently to the ground. The person or persons rushed on, out and into the fog. The door slammed.

The store was empty. Everything was still. The old woman lay in a heap, bewildered and in pain. Gradually she began to know that someone or some people had rushed out into the fog, knocking her down and hurting her because she happened to be in the way. She whimpered and she thought badly of Wong Kee because he did not come to help her. Her body gave her massive pain, and as she looked slowly about her in a stupefied way she saw that a number of heavy cans of food had rained down upon her and lay around her. As she tried clumsily to heave herself up (but that was not possible), a customer came in.

"Well well well!" said the customer bending over her, "whatever . . . " then straightened himself and listened. A faint sound as of a bubbling sigh came from behind the counter on which was the till. The till was open and empty. The customer went behind the counter and again bent down. Then he drew himself up quickly. Wong Kee lay like a bundle of old clothes from which blood seeped and spread. The sound that the customer had heard was the soft sound of the death of Wong Kee who was an honest man and innocent. He had worked all his life and had robbed no one. He had an old wife who loved him. In a way hard to explain they were seriously and simply happy together. This was now over.

The customer paid no further attention to Mrs. Bylow on the floor but, stepping round Wong Kee's body, reached the telephone.

A small woman parted the dingy curtains which separated

the store from the home of Wong Kee and his wife. She held in her arms a bundle of stove wood and stood motionless like a wrinkled doll. Then the stove wood clattered to the ground and she dropped to her knees uttering high babbling noises. She rocked and prostrated herself beside the impossible sight of her husband's dead body and his blood. The customer regarded her as he talked into the telephone. Then he too knelt down and put his arm round her. He could find nothing to say but the immemorial "There, there . . . "

Mrs. Bylow, lying neglected on the floor, endeavoured to look behind her but she had to realize as people do in bombardment, flood, and earthquake that she was at the mercy of whatever should happen to her and could not do anything about it, let alone look behind her.

"They're slow coming," said the customer. "It's the fog."

The old Chinese woman wrenched herself from him. "I tarryphome," she cried out, "I tarryphome my son. . . . "

The door opened and there seemed to be some policemen. The outside fog poured in with this entrance and some other kind of fog pressed down upon Mrs. Bylow's understanding and blurred it. "I'm a very old woman," she mumbled to a constable who had a little book, "and they knocked me down . . . they mighta killed me . . . they shouldn't a done that . . . they've broke my hip . . . aah . . . !"

"Yes lady, we'll look after you," said the constable, "Who was it?"

"It was . . ."(well, who was it?) "I guess it was some man . . . no . . ." she breathed with difficulty, she should not have to suffer so, "I guess it was a boy . . . no, two boys . . . they knocked me down. . . . "

A constable at the door said to a crowd which had gathered from somewhere in the fog and now pushed against the front of the store, "Now then, you can't come in here, there's been a robbery, see? You best go on home," but someone battered on the pane with both hands enough to break it, and Miss Casey burst in at the door, her red hair wet with fog.

"She's here! Yes there she is!" said Miss Casey talking to everyone in her loud voice and bringing into the muted shop a blazing of bright eyes and hair and leopard coat and humanity, " – that's what I thought! I thought right after I left the store I'd better go in and see was she O.K. because she shouldn't be out and the fog was just *awful* and I prett' near went past her gate but I kinda felt something was wrong and my goodness see what happened. . . . Mrs. Bylow honey, what happened to you," and Miss Casey dropped on her knees and took Mrs. Bylow's hand in hers. "Say, what's been going on around here, anyway?" she said, looking up at the constable ready to accuse.

"She's not so good," said the constable in a low tone in Mrs. Bylow's dream and a high noise came into the night ("That's the syreen," said Miss Casey) and some men lifted her and took her somewhere on a bed. It did not occur to Mrs. Bylow that perhaps she had been killed inadvertantly by two youths who had just killed her old friend, but if a policeman had said to her, "Now you are dead," she would have accepted the information, so unfamiliar was the experience of boring horizontally through a fog at top speed very slowly in a high and unexplained swelling noise. She opened her eyes and saw a piece of Miss Casey's leopard coat and so she was not dead.

"Is it reel?" she whispered, because she had always wanted to know. "Is what reel?" said Miss Casey bending her flaming head. "Sure it's reel. The collar's reel anyway." Mrs. Bylow closed her eyes again for several years and said, "But I never got my cocoa." Then she began to cry quietly because she felt old and helpless and the pain was something cruel but it was good to feel Miss Casey beside her in her leopard coat. She did not know that Wong Kee was dead — slugged on the head, pistol-whipped, stabbed again and again in the stomach with a long knife — all because he had summoned his small strength and fought like a cat and defended himself for his right to his thirty dollars and some loose change and a handful of cigarettes and his life. "Well, here we are," said Miss Casey, standing up, very cheerful.

In a week or two, while she was better and before she got worse, Mrs. Bylow began to remember the two boys whom she had never seen and, as she constructed their leather jackets and their faces, she said she would know them anywhere. Of course she would not, and the murderers of Wong Kee were never found but carried the knowledge of their murder into the fog with them on their way from the betrayal of their youth to whatever else they would soon violently undertake to do. When they arrived back, each at his own home, their parents said in pursuance of their habit of long years past, "Where you bin?" and the hoodlums said in pursuance of their habit of long years past, "Out." This satisfied the idiot parents. They said, "My that fog's just terrible," and the hoodlums said, "Sure is." They were excited and nervous because this was the first time they had killed, but they had the money. One of the young hoodlums did not go into the room where his parents were but went upstairs because he was pretty sure there was still some blood on his hands and so there was. Wong Kee's blood was on his parents' hands too but they, being irresponsible, did not know this. And on their hands was the blood of Mrs. Bylow who was soon to die, and of Mrs. Wong Kee who could no longer be said to live, and of their own hoodlum children.

Before Mrs. Bylow died, wiped out by forces quite outside herself like a moth in a storm (not much more and no less), she began to be a little proud of almost being present at a murder.

"It's not everyone who's been at a murder, Miss Casey, love, is it?"

"No honey," said Miss Casey, seeing again that sordid scene, "it isn't everyone."

"I always liked that coat of yours," said Mrs. Bylow.

"And then," said Miss Casey to Mrs. Merkle, "d'you know what she said? She said if ever I come to die — just like she wasn't ever going to — would you please wear your leopard coat. She's crazy about that coat. And then she said she often thought of those two boys that killed the storekeeper and knocked her down and she guessed it was more their parents' fault and not their fault. It made the tears come to your eyes," said Miss Casey who was kind as well as noisy and cherished a sense of personal drama.

"Sure," said Mrs. Merkle who had eyes like marbles that did not weep.

Mrs. Bylow's death was obscure and pitiful. Miss Casey got the afternoon off and so there were two people at her funeral. Miss Casey wore her leopard coat as promised.

Making a Sale
Evans Thordarson

It was July 22nd but it was cold and wet, and the three figures crouched in front of the machine shed wore parkas. They were replacing sections on a worn mower sickle. The shed, a sagging unpainted pile of boards, had once been an extension to a barn but the parent building had fallen down years before. Over the years the rafters and siding had been broken up for firewood or dragged across the yard to the wood saw mounted on an old high-wheeled wagon, and when enough pressure had been exerted by the woman in the house, the tractor was started and driven to the saw and jockeyed into position. Then when the belt had been rolled out and stretched taut, the high-pitched whine of the saw blade cutting through the knotty wood could be heard above the roar of the tractor.

The shed was open at the end where the barn had been and

wide enough to drive the tractor in for some protection from the snow and rain; the back end protruded because boxes and tubs of rusty nuts and bolts and salvaged parts of worn-out machinery were scattered on the ground at the front end of the building.

The three were squatted around an anvil. The old one, maybe fifty-five, big and rough in his greasy overalls, knees sticking out, wielded the hammer. The other two, fourteen or fifteen but already adult in their resignation to life, looked the same; dressed in blue jeans, not so dirty as the old ones' as if age determined colour, but replicas of the faded coat and battered grey hat. One was supporting the end of the sickle and the other one watching; their shoulders hunched from the wet wind which promised the July rains were not ready to end.

As they worked, the sound from the hammer rang through the rambling yard, across the weeded area that should have been a lawn, to the curtainless windows of the house.

"What's that coming?" the old one asked, turning his head and half rising to get a better view of the road that wound along the coulee bank a few hundred yards in front of the buildings. The first young one, the one who had been watching, rose to look across the prairie, squinting through his dirty glasses. The other young one, sitting on the ground with the mower sickle across his legs, simply stretched his neck crane-like, straightening his shoulders to add two or three inches to his height.

A small, brightly painted red tractor appeared from behind the line of poplar trees that obscured the far end of the road. The tractor was creeping towards the farm; a faint whining of gears sounded above the engine.

"It's Franklyn!"

"No," the old one spoke. "That's Oscar Johnson with his C. He's probably bringing it out here to sell it to us," he added dryly, pushing the sickle back against the anvil. "I guess he's afraid he won't get a good price at the auction so he's going to try to sell it to us before. That's just the sort of sneak I've always told you he was."

"We need a small tractor for the rake!"

The old one roughly jerked the sickle ahead. "He'll want too much for it," he grunted as he swung the hammer. There was a disappointed silence.

"Look at him come now!"

The hum of the engine had become a full-throated roar.

The second young one rose to a kneeling position to look down the road.

"Hold the knife still!" The authority in the command brought both young ones back to the ground and they were silent. But the old one's severe manner did not last.

"Hello, Oscar!" he called over his shoulder when the tractor pulled into the yard and the engine fell silent. A foolish grin swept across his face and his motions became exaggerated as he continued working.

"How are you fellows?" Oscar greeted them slowly, moving his bulky frame towards the three.

The first young one got up to meet him. "What are you doing with the tractor?"

"Oh, I've just had the engine overhauled and I wanted to see how it runs."

The work continued, with Oscar watching what had now become an exhibition of skill. His freshly starched railroad cap and clean overalls contrasted sharply with the clothing the three wore. He watched, only interrupting to comment on the workmanship. However, the old one spoke, grunting between the hammer blows:

"The blacksmith charges fifteen dollars for a job like this." The words were clipped by the hammer. "I can do it in an hour."

"Yes, anything you get done nowadays costs a fortune." Oscar spoke seriously in a whispering, confidential tone. "You can't afford to have equipment that's going to take a lot of repairs."

"There's no question about that."

"It must cost you a lot though. You put up a lot of hay." Oscar's voice made the statement flattering.

"You could say that," the old one replied. He looked up grinning, his face red from the exertion. "We'll be haying right into harvest time again this year." There was a note of pride rather than discouragement in his tone.

"Your hay is very good. You can't afford to leave any of it uncut." Oscar shook his head as he spoke and again the whispering, confiding note had crept into his voice. "Are you going to sell any this year?"

"Yes, and we'll get it all up, even if I have to fight to get these two out of bed and to work every morning. We don't need ten men to put up a few fork fulls of hay like our neighbours." He spoke derisively but proudly. The words rising and striking with the hammer. He paused while he fitted the last section into place. "This is the hardest one to put in. Most people never get it tight."

Oscar watched closely.

"Yes, everyone knows that we have the best hay land. There, that does it. The knife's as good as new." As the old one raised himself stiffly from the ground, he continued. "I've sacrificed enough to get that land. The best cattle and hay land around here, and people thought I was crazy to buy it, when they were all greedy to raise wheat. But now they come begging me for hay. Well, they'll have to pay the same as everyone else for it."

"Yes, you've got a big business built up here, but for an operation like yours you have to be well-equipped . . . you have to make hay while the sun shines." Oscar chuckled at his own humour.

The old one was holding the seven-foot sickle at arm's length, squinting along it to gauge the evenness of the sections.

"Look'it, Oscar, what do you think of this for a job?" He thrust one end in front of Oscar.

"Yes, perfect." The knife was still whipping back and forth.

"I don't think you saw it well enough. Here, take another look."

The sickle was again held up for Oscar's inspection and this time he deliberated longer, running his hand along the back of the knife and squinting once or twice at the glimmering perfect row the sections made.

The young ones had walked over to the tractor and were circling it, kicking the tires and feeling the rubber lugs, looking at the small engine that sat awkwardly sideways on the frame. They tested the steering by reaching up and giving the wheel a few half turns, first one way, then the other. They stepped back and regarded the machine at a distance as the old one started his tour followed at a pace or two by Oscar.

"It must be rough to ride." The old one looked meaningfully at the young ones as he spoke. He continued his tour, mocking the little tractor good-naturedly. "It's so light that if it hit a coyote hole it would flip over backwards." At the remark the young ones tried rocking the front end.

"Franklyn's is the same and he uses his on the mower," Oscar remarked casually.

The young ones had taken positions by the front wheels and, gripping the axle, made a combined effort to lift the tractor.

"Oh don't worry, you can't." Oscar was more serious. After a final supreme effort they retired a few feet and regarded the machine with more respect.

"I guess if we're going to get all that hay up we'll need another tractor for the rake." The old one spoke as he rested his hand against the back of the driver's seat. "I suppose we'll have to rent one from the garage in town." He looked at the young ones who waited anxiously.

"It would be better to have our own," the first young one

interjected. The old one settled his gaze on him, then turned to Oscar.

"Will you sell us the tractor?"

"I can't." The words fell into a heavy silence, killing the young one's growing excitement. "It's listed on the auction sale posters so it will have to be sold along with everything else at the sale next Saturday."

The old one looked at Oscar, almost incredulously. "How much do you think you'll get for it?"

"Well," Oscar paused thoughtfully. "It should bring four hundred or four hundred and fifty dollars; there's a good demand for little tractors at this time of the year."

"It's a good tractor and we sure need it, but I couldn't go above three fifty." The old one shook his head.

"I'd like to see you get it," Oscar replied. "We've been good friends for a long time and you certainly need it if you're going to get all that hay up."

The young ones listened, desperately hoping that a way could be found out of the dilemma.

"No, I'm afraid there's nothing that can be done about the tractor," Oscar spoke sadly. "But I'll tell you what," he confided. "You've always been a man of your word! You put in a three hundred and fifty dollar bid to get things going and I'll hold out some of the saws and tools you want. You can also take that pile of old lumber. And you never can tell — " Oscar winked slyly at the three "— you might get the tractor at that price."

"That's the least I can do for an old friend like you, Oscar, when you're leaving the country. It will get the bidding off to a good start and we can sure use that lumber to build some new sheds. It will serve those neighbours of ours right, too; I can't afford the tractor but we can make sure none of them will get it for a song." The old one was smiling. "Let's go in and have some coffee . . . it was cold sitting on the ground."

The others nodded in agreement and trooped off through the weeds to the house.

Saturday, the day of the auction sale, was grey and raining and the usual excitement that pervades a sale did not appear to brighten the day. It was a small affair. Oscar had quit farming years previously and only retained the few small implements required to work the field he had been forced to buy when he had taken over as postmaster of the village and purchased the house and lean-to that served the community's postal requirements. A good collection of carpentry tools was offered to the few people who gathered, mostly through curiosity and habit, but the major item was the tractor. Even this failed to create much excitement.

At precisely two o'clock the auctioneer, who had driven out from the neighbouring town, mounted his box and started the sale with a low yodel. First the boxes of saws, hammers, wood-planes and other tools were offered. The sale proceeded slowly with bids of fifty cents and a dollar for individual items, the auctioneer coaxing the last nickel out of the knot of bidders and spectators moved to buy the farm implements: a seeder with attachments, a cultivator, four harrow sections, a rubber-tired trailer, and the tractor.

"Okay boys! We'll start with the trailer and box." The auctioneer stepped up onto a wheel and swung himself into the box. "Who's gonna start the bidding?" The last two words ran into his yodel. "And who's gonna bid me twenty-five, twenty-five, where's twenty-five?"

"Twenty, I've got twenty, who's gonna give another five?" he yodeled. "Bid twenty and where's five, five, five, who's gonna give me five?" The yodel rose and fell. The trailer was sold; then the seeder and cultivator, followed by the harrow sections, and only the tractor was left.

"Boys, this is the minute you've all been waiting for. You've all had a chance to look the tractor over and there's no need for me to explain what uses a handy little machine like this can be put to. It's not new, but you all know Oscar and how he looks after everything he has; you all know his wife Eliza." The men around him were still chuckling at the allusion to Eliza's weight when he raised his voice: "Now let's get started."

The old one was there, waiting expectantly at the edge of the crowd.

"Where'd you want to start, boys? Who's gonna give me the first bid?" The old one waited nervously. His instructions were to wait for the bidding to start, then put in competitive bids until he reached three hundred and fifty dollars. "Bida, bid, bid . . . who's gonna give me a bid? . . . . bida, bid, bid, boys let's get going! Who's gonna start things out . . .?"

"Hundred and seventy-five here!" It was Arthur Jeffs who farmed a small piece of land on the edge of the village.

"I've got one seventy-five, who's gonna bid two?" The auctioneer's voice rose shrilly on this point. "Boys, you're not gonna stand there and watch this tractor go without putting a bid on it. Who's gonna give me two?"

"Two hundred!" the old one bid.

"Two hundred, that's better. . . . I'm bid two hundred dollars, who's gonna make it a quarter? Two, two, two! Who's got a quarter? Boys, you've all seen the tractor. Some of you were driving it around here before the sale started. Why, I even drove it myself. I've got a good mind to buy it and just park it in my yard at home. It's worth two and a quarter just to look at . . . Now who's going to bid a quarter?" The auctioneer's words were slow and beads of perspiration stood out on his forehead. "Last chance. Who's going to give me a bid?"

"Two ten." It was Arthur Jeffs again.

"Two ten. Are there any other bids? Going, going . . ."

"Three hundred and fifty!"

The auctioneer stopped dead; his eyes shot over the group of men. "What was that bid?"

"Three hundred and fifty dollars," the old one repeated quietly; all eyes were now turned towards him and the two young ones who stood one at either side. The auctioneer, still standing on the tractor, his heavy jowls purple from the exertion of the sales, the smile fading from his face at the awkwardness of the moment, worked his throat drily once.

"Sold!" he finally stammered.

Oscar pushed his way through the men, ignoring the suddenly changed atmosphere till he reached the three standing defiantly where the crowd parted.

"Well, there wasn't much interest in the tractor today. This weather discourages the boys."

"That just shows what fools they all are. Haven't I always told you they were?" the old one whispered. "They'll need a tractor like this all the more when the rain stops."

The young ones stared straight at Oscar.

"The wife can drive the truck. I'll take the tractor now if it's all right with you, Oscar."

"Yes! Yes, of course it's all right. I'll drive out tonight and we can settle up then."

The old one climbed onto the seat and pressed the starter button. The men watched him drive off with the two young ones standing one on each side of the drawbar.

Letter from Sakaye
Beverley Mitchell

I found the letter from Sakaye today when I was looking through a box of old books in the basement. It was stuck between the pages of my Sunday School Bible, and at first I didn't recognize it. After nearly thirty years, the cheap wartime newsprint is worn and creased, and the writing just barely legible — but I can still make out most of it, even if it is in pencil. Besides, I don't think I've ever forgotten it — and I know I've never forgotten Sakaye. She wrote the letter just after she'd been sent away, and I can remember how excited I was to find it waiting for me when I came home from school — how disappointed I was because she didn't really say anything. Just that she was living on a farm on the prairies now and she missed Mission, and she wondered if Billy Hunter was sitting in her old desk behind me, and had Mrs. Grimsby come for rehearsals yet, and who was to be the new May Queen. Nothing really important in that. At least, that's what I thought nearly thirty years ago — and I can't remember if I ever answered it. I didn't think then that Mrs. Grimsby or Billy Hunter was important enough to bother about. And I didn't realize when I was eleven how important I was to Sakaye — and I didn't know how important she was to me. That's one of the hardest things about growing older — remembering all the opportunities you missed because you didn't have the understanding to appreciate them when they were offered — and then realizing when you do have the understanding, that it's too late.

I suppose our relationship started on the first day of school in Grade One. That was the same year the CPR Empress liner nearing Shanghai at the end of her voyage was turned back to Honolulu without even going into the Shanghai harbour — and the people on the ship could see smoke rising from the buildings as the Japanese planes dropped their bombs. Some of the passengers were businessmen returning to their families, and some were the wives and children of businessmen whose offices were not far from the harbour. . . .

In Mission City the desks in the Grade One classroom were shining with new varnish that smelled sickly-sweet, and the floor was slippery from the fresh oil the janitor had coated it with during the summer holidays. I sat at my desk, hugging the wonder that I was finally a school-girl with a desk of my own, with a fresh bottle of white paste stuck in the inkwell and a board to rest my feet on if they got tired on the floor. There were pictures all around the room and charts and blackboards with real chalk and new erasers and a sandtable with real sand in the corner and a small table at the back of the room with little red chairs — and books open on the table and on the shelves. And piled on the ledge beside the teacher's desk were boxes of plasticine — coloured plasticine. And the smell! The delicious grown-up smell of chalk dust and oil and the teacher's perfume and rubber erasers and soap and my new school bag. The teacher was busy writing the names of pupils who hadn't registered, questioning the mothers who were a straggly, whispering group beside her desk. We sat in awed silence, overwhelmed by the strangeness and importance of being in school. I could see my mother standing at the back of the room with the rest of the parents who had finished registering, and when she caught my eye, she smiled.

Margaret Barry sat a few desks up in the next row, swinging her foot very carefully in the aisle so everyone would notice her new school shoes, and Billy Hunter was scrunched in front of me, furiously uncomfortable in a starched white shirt and bow tie. I didn't know all the kids, but most of them looked as excited as I felt. I poked Billy Hunter on the shoulder to show him my new school bag, and we were just undoing the buckle when I noticed the little girl beside me. There were no sleeves in her cotton dress and her arms were covered with goose pimples — and she was sitting perfectly still, wrapped in an envelope of private misery and crying without making any sound. Billy and I stared at her, astonished that anyone would cry on the first day of school, and in front of all the kids. She wasn't very big — and the tips of her canvas shoes just reached the floor. I could see the splotch marks on her desk from tears, and while we watched, more tears splashed off her cheeks. Suddenly my mother came down the aisle. She squeezed herself into the little desk beside the girl and put her arm around her. Billy and I could hear her whispering that when she had been a teacher and Sakaye's brother was a little boy, she had taught him in this very room. So that was her name — Sakaye. Billy and I looked at each other — we'd never known anyone with a name like that. And when my mother pointed to me and told Sakaye that I was her little girl and Billy Hunter was my friend, Sakaye glanced at us shyly and then looked down at her desk again. She sat there huddled against my mother, not crying anymore, but not looking around, either.

I guess my mother made Billy and me feel protective towards Sakaye from the beginning, because when Margaret Barry and some of the other kids started to giggle at Sakaye for being a baby and at my mother squeezed into a Grade One desk, Billy and I just glared them into silence. And we didn't laugh when Sakaye refused to tell the teacher her name, and my mother answered for her and pointed out Sakaye's brother, standing at the back of the room with the parents. I hadn't relized that my mother had taught in my Grade One class-room and I hadn't realized she had taught someone as interesting as Sakaye's brother. I'm afraid it made me feel quite important to know all that.

It made me important in Sakaye's eyes, too. I think she always liked me because of my mother — and sometimes when we were playing in the yard at recess she would come and stand beside me without saying anything. She never said anything in Grade One — not even when it was her turn to read out loud. I knew she understood English, but she wouldn't ever say anything in English at school. She was smart, though — she always got a gold star on her paper for number work, and her printing was so good the teacher would put it on the board for everyone to see. That pleased me. Somehow I felt that it was because my mother had taught Sakaye's brother that she was so smart. And I didn't mind it when I had to take Sakaye to the girls' bathroom in the basement and show her how to use the toilet. That was after she had wet her pants one afternoon during printing.

We must have been going to school for at least a month then, because most of the novelty had worn off and I was sitting uncomfortably correct for printing: back straight, feet together on the floor, in the exact centre of my seat, scribbler making a diagonal with the top left of the page and arm resting loosely on the desk — loosely, Miss MacDonald insisted — and the right hand holding the pencil loosely so it rested on the joint of the first finger. Rested loosely. Miss MacDonald crept around the room, up and down the aisles, swooping down on you suddenly from behind and flicking your pencil or jogging your left arm. If the pencil flew out of your hand you had been holding it correctly; and if your left arm slithered across your desk, knocking your scribbler to the floor, that had been the correct printing position. My neck and shoulders ached from the dreadful effort of keeping my left arm and right hand loose, and the circles I was making were woefully inconsistent — some above and below the blue lines, some not even touching the lines. The classroom was unusually quiet, save for the whisper of pencils on paper and the tiptoe tread of Miss MacDonald.

When I first heard it, it was like the slow sibilant hiss of an old steam pipe which increased in volume and persistence to the first splash and steady drumming on the floor. It was coming from Sakaye's desk — and when I looked over I saw that the last of the perfectly formed, loose, round circles on her page was wandering uncertainly above and below the blue lines, as the puddle kept growing and growing under her desk, and little yellow rivulets spread in all directions on her seat, dripping down the back and running down the cast-iron scrollwork at the side. It seemed to last forever, and all the time Sakaye kept making her pencil go round and round the last circle, which wasn't a circle at all. The kids began to snicker — I almost laughed myself. Not because Sakaye had wet her pants — that was horrible — but because Margaret Barry was making frantic and futile efforts to keep her new school shoes out of the puddle which had spread all the way to her desk.

Miss MacDonald came down the aisle to see what the commotion was all about. I guess when she saw the size of the puddle she realized that Sakaye hadn't been to the bathroom for a long, long time. She wasn't mad or anything. "Sakaye, why didn't you put your hand up if you had to leave the room?"

We had this elaborate system of hand signals in Grade One. If your hand was up, that meant you wanted to ask a question. Your hand up with one finger showing meant you had to leave the room, but it would only take a few minutes. Hand up with two fingers involved a longer absence. Sakaye didn't answer Miss MacDonald.

"Sakaye, do you know where the girls' toilet is?" This in a whisper from Miss MacDonald. Still no answer from Sakaye, but she stopped making the desperate circle and shook her head. "Jennifer will show you."

So that's how I came to take Sakaye down to the girls' bathroom in the basement for the rest of Grade One, and I suppose that's when we really became friends. She never did put her hand up to leave the room, but when she had to go, she'd reach over and tap my arm gently and I'd understand and put up my hand with its important one finger in plain view.

I was scared of the girls' basement — especially in the afternoon after the janitor had swept the floor and sunlight streaming through the little high window swam dizzily through the swirling dust particles. The cement on the floor wasn't quite even and the shadows and dusty light chutes gave me the feeling that I was half floating. And noises from the classrooms above us echoed with terrifying intensity — the clatter of rulers dropping, the heavy measured tread of a teacher's feet, and the distorted voices coming from a great distance. But I couldn't let Sakaye see how scared I was. She had taken my hand when we left the Grade One classroom, and we crept down the old wooden stairs that creaked with each step. She didn't seem to mind having wet her pants once we got out of the classroom, and I had the impression that she was rather pleased to be away from it all.

The worst thing about the girls' basement was the fact that the toilets flushed automatically — and, to me, unpredictably — with a thunderous swoosh of water. That and the smell: Lysol so strong it grabbed my throat and gagged me — and the horrible green soap in the dispenser, and wet paper towels and orange peels and apple cores in the waste basket.

When we reached the little room with the toilets behind their swinging wooden doors, I pushed one open to show Sakaye where it was. They were all innocently quiet. When I realized that Sakaye didn't even know how to sit on one, there was nothing for me to do but demonstrate. Sure enough, while I was sitting there explaining, all the toilets flushed together. It really wasn't as bad as I had imagined — just a little cold and windy on my bottom — but it still frightened me half to death. I couldn't let Sakaye see *that*. But after the first expression of amazement had widened her eyes, she began to laugh. Politely, of course, and she put both hands over her mouth so she wouldn't offend me. But I knew she thought that I had made all that thunderous swoosh. I guess I started to giggle, too, and after I had finished what the fright made me do, I made her sit on the little wooden seat. And I made her stay there until the toilets flushed again, and when the cold wind reached her bottom we both started to giggle helplessly all over again. It was really kind of fun — naughty fun, perhaps — but fun, nevertheless. After the first time, she would never close the swinging door behind her when we made our daily visits, but she had me stand where she could see me. We always giggled — but Sakaye still wouldn't say anything, not even to me. . . .

I can't remember anything about Sakaye in Grade Two. Perhaps she wasn't in my class that year, or perhaps the Grade Two teacher took a dim view of two little girls leaving the room at once. I just can't remember now. But it's strange that Sakaye should ask about Mrs. Grimsby and Billy Hunter and the May Queen in her letter, because what I remember of her in Grade Three is inextricably linked with them. . . .

Mrs. Grimsby was the official accompanist. Come the end of April, she appeared with inexorable regularity at the old grey annex which served as the elementary school gym. The janitor would have nailed the scarred and battered May pole to the centre of the gym floor and screwed the wooden circle with its old coloured streamers into the top. In many ways, Mrs. Grimsby was very like the old May pole: she was grey with a certain battered dignity; she was much smaller at the top than at the bottom; and the emblem on her Legion tam had the same faded droop as the May pole streamers. She always wore her Legion Auxiliary uniform for rehearsals.

A few days before Mrs. Grimsby came for rehearsals, we would have a series of "dry runs" in the gym. First we would be paired off with the boys according to height. Then we would line up in the corner, holding hands, and walk to the May pole. I always got paired off with Billy Hunter. By Grade Three, my relationship with Billy had undergone a subtle change. Deep down we were still good friends, but certain things about Billy bothered me in Grade Three. For one thing, he had not taken to school with the same gusto I had, and was afraid of the teachers. Of all teachers, not just Miss Buckley, who terrified everyone. For another, he had very sweaty hands. I suppose it was the sweaty hands that bothered me most. If Miss Buckley glared at Billy, the perspiration oozed from his palms in direct proportion to the height of her impatience. A little glare, a little sweat; a big glare, a big sweat; a glare and a shout, a veritable flood. In the middle of the walk from the corner of the gym to the May pole I would slip and slither in the frantic clutch of Billy's sweating hand until he would finally snatch it away and wipe it on his pants. Miss Buckley would bark at him and he'd grab me and leak horribly all over my hand for the rest of the rehearsal.

The dry runs were never much fun. Miss Buckley would bang time with a ruler and we'd walk around the May pole, in and out singly, then in and out in pairs, until she would be satisfied that the majority of us had at least a dim idea of what we were doing. Then would come the skipping — dust would fly up from the floor, the old gym would shake, and we'd all be red from exertion. And Billy's hands would sweat. If we were really smart, we'd get to use the streamers the first day. Usually it was the second. Or the third. If we had dared, we would have tangled the ribbons on purpose, just to watch Miss Buckley get mad. But we didn't dare — and the knots and tangles that sometimes needed the janitor to get them undone were the result of sheer ignorance.

By the time Mrs. Grimsby came to the rehearsals, we were fairly good. She'd be sitting at the piano waiting for us when we came in ranks from our classroom, the shiny seat of her Legion Auxiliary skirt firmly settled on the piano bench and the emblem on her Legion Auxiliary tam quivering expectantly until she got the nod form Miss Buckley to begin "Come Lasses and Lads". With the first bar, Mrs. Grimsby would undergo some kind of mystical transformation — the greying figure in the old blue uniform would swell visibly until she became Boadicea leading the British Empire in the paths of glory. "Come Lasses and *thump,* take leave of your *thump,* and away to the May pole *thump."* And away we'd go magnificently until the dust from our banging feet swirled in giddy, ecstatic clouds.

But this is where Sakaye comes in again. Half the pupils in my Grade Three class were Japanese and they hated the May pole dancing. If one of the Japanese boys had to have a white girl for a partner, he'd squeeze her fingers until they were white and then stick his fingernails in the soft flesh. We didn't dare tell on them because we were almost as frightened of them as we were of Miss Buckley. So the boys were never punished. But the girls were. Miss Buckley would be driven to near maniacal frenzy by the fact that Japanese etiquette demanded the girls never walk with the boys but follow them from a humble distance. She would shrill at them, making a rainbow of saliva that half-delighted, half-terrified us — but it didn't have much effect on the Japanese girls. They would skip obediently — but still just a trifle behind their partners. And Miss Buckley would spank them, turning them over her knee in front of everyone and smacking them with the ruler until her arm was tired. She never hit one of us, so we could only guess how much it hurt.

By Grade Three we were used to the heavy orange and green socks the Japanese girls wore with their cheap canvas shoes, and we took the cotton dresses they wore on even the coldest days as a matter of course. But when they were turned over Miss Buckley's knee and we saw the heavy flour sack petticoats and panties — still with *purity* stamped on them — and stitched together with coloured yarn, we were shocked. We could tell that Mrs Grimsby didn't like it either, because she'd sit rigid at the piano — and when she played after someone had been spanked the music sounded different, *"Come* lasses and thump". The day that Sakaye was spanked, Billy and I stood there holding hands, and I didn't even mind that his was sweaty and trembling. But we were in Grade Three then, and there was nothing we could do except look away and pretend that we hadn't noticed anything. I think Sakaye understood — but even in Grade Three she wouldn't say anything in English — and I just couldn't find anything to say to her. My mother didn't say anything, either, when I told her — but I still remember the expression on her face. I saw the same expression on Mrs. Grimsby's face three years later one Sunday in the United Church — and recalling all this now, I have suddenly realized that Miss Buckley's ruler was somehow responsible for my leaving the church when I was eleven.

The Japanese had their own United Church up on the hill behind the fair grounds. Their minister was a white woman who had spent most of her life as a missionary in Japan, so that even her walk resembled the obsequious shuffle of the Japanese women. I found her fascinating — not that she made any effort to become friendly with the ladies of the white congregation — but fascinating from the fact that when she did stop to talk to my mother, her English had a peculiar singsong intonation. And when she met her Japanese parishioners on Main Street, she would make three jerky Oriental bows to the men — not to the women — before speaking to them. And the quality of the respect she got from the Japanese youngsters in my class impressed me. She taught them in their own language for two hours after school in the plain grey building that was also their church, and whenever they met her down town on Saturdays I would see them bowing very politely from the waist — three times, just like their fathers. They would stand in shy groups talking to her, before whirling off like autumn leaves just as gay in their bright colours, and just as elusive. Apart from Sakaye, who would half-wave if she saw us, I never really got to know any of them — nobody did. They came from a world that was different from any we white children knew, and they endured ours for the five hours they had to be in school — then they were off. I used to wonder what they did — but they would never say. Sometimes I think that by the time we had all reached Grade Five, the girls might have talked with us — but if one of the boys noticed a girl talking to us, he would snap at her in Japanese and that would be the end of it.

Their minister tried to explain their culture to the Ladies Auxiliary, and came to one of their meetings with lantern slides. But I guess no one was really interested, because she tried only once. She offered to show them to my Sunday School class, too, but Mrs. Hancock was our teacher that year, and she was interested in the mission in India. I don't think Sakaye ever knew about Mrs. Hancock, and I'm sure Mrs. Hancock didn't know Sakaye — and Mrs. Hancock made it plain to everyone that she barely tolerated the Japanese minister. But the minister came to a few of the suppers the women put on in the basement of the church, and she always looked rather out of place among the potato salads and pumpkin pies and cold ham and pickles — and the women in aprons, red with exertion and Christian fellowship, and the men with cigars, and the kids running around and squabbling.

There were always squabbles at the church suppers, and too much food, and too much smoke and too much noise. And we always had to clap for Mrs. Hancock, because she had worked so hard and washed so many dishes and done so many wonderful Christian things. And Mrs. Hancock would accept all this homage as if it really were her due, smoothing down the pink ruffled apron she had made and then bought back at the bazaar, her powerful hands red and wrinkled from the dish water. Beside Mrs. Hancock, the Japanese minister was dwarfed almost to the point of oblivion. Mrs. Hancock was a big woman — but she contained herself admirably with a corset which must have been in constant struggle with her rebellious flesh. Even when she sat down we could hear the battle going on with mysterious creakings underneath her dress, on which the ridges of whale bone stood out in full relief. Althought I still can't really forgive Mrs. Hancock, I suppose I must give her her due — she must have suffered like the early martyrs in that corset. Her corset didn't always triumph over her flesh, either. Frequently the interior turmoil was made audible in explosions of sound that even today I have a grudging admiration for.

Like a boiler taxed to the point of explosion, it would start with deep intestinal rumblings — heavy at first, then a series of stacatto thumps a high whining soprano as it reached her great bosom — then brawpp. Oh, a magnificient brawpp! Followed by "My Jesus, mercy." Why she called on the merciful Jesus, we never quite understood, but she must have astonished even Him. Over the clatter of knives and forks as the women set the bare plank tables, and the crash of lids on the old stove, and the thundering of us youngsters as we ran back and forth unsupervised on the stage, it would echo magnificiently. "Brawpp. My Jesus, mercy." There would be a few seconds of awed silence — even the grownups were impressed — or startled — and then the women would clatter just a little louder, and the men's voices would rise politely in an effort to appear as if they had noticed nothing. It was useless, of course, because the lovely thing about Mrs. Hancock's gas attacks was that once they started they kept right on. And we knew it. The scuffling on the stage would stop abruptly — even the kids who were fighting about Chopsticks on the piano would abandon their position — and we would all melt quietly to the kitchen door. Mrs. Hancock's performance made the church suppers worth coming to as far as we were concerned. We would squeeze ourselves against the wall and wait fascinated for the next eruption, not even daring to laugh for fear we'd miss something.

The highlight of Mrs. Hancock's religious experiences, as she told her Sunday school classes with unfailing and relentless regularity, had been a minister's sermon on the holy women in the gospel. Why it had impressed her I never knew, for a more boring and stupid existence than theirs I couldn't imagine. But watching Mrs. Hancock washing dishes in the church basement I could see that she really fancied herself as *the* holy woman of the gospels, trudging after Jesus and His disciples, and washing their dirty socks and cooking their meals. Somewhere down the years Mrs. Hancock had forgotten they were originally *women,* and she seemed determined to do her Christian ministrations all by herself. At least, that's what it looked like to us watching from the door. There were always crowds of flustered women in the kitchen, basting turkeys and spooning pickles out of jars, and slicing homemade bread. But Mrs. Hancock was the Queen Bee, and made the others insignificant as drones. It would be one of the drones — usually my mother or Mrs. Grimsby — who would notice us at the door, and make us move reluctantly to the other end of the hall, "out of the way".

The Japanese minister had been invited to the last church

supper I attended, and spent most of her time at the small sink in the corner, scrubbing cocoa out of the blue enamel pots that had to be used for coffee. She seemed unmoved by either the fluster of the women or the importance of Mrs. Hancock — and her face was as tranquilly impassive then as it was later when she clapped politely. I saw her shuffle out quietly in the grey cloth coat she wore to church functions, and I don't think the others even knew she had gone. That must have been the last time I saw her, because a few weeks later after that was the attack on Pearl Harbour. . . .

Pearl Harbour was the event that really shattered our illusion on the West Coast that the war was "over there". The *Eine Kleine Nachtmusik,* pale flames in December sunlight, Sunday afternoon security — all are linked irrevocably in my memories of Pearl Harbour. I was eleven then. The sun was streaming through the windows in the living room while I sat half-asleep in an armchair watching the flames in the fireplace and waiting for my grandparents to wake up from their Sunday afternoon nap. My father was dozing on the chesterfield and my mother was reading peacefully — no one was really listening to the symphony on the radio. The sudden interruption of the music startled us — and I could tell from the expression on my father's face that there was something frightening in the announcer's terse message. It was over almost as soon as it began — the sun was still shining, the fire purring quietly, and again, after the announcer's voice, the Mozart. But something was irretrievably lost — perhaps it was security, perhaps it was the illusion that our lives were contained in the small world that was the family — perhaps it was something too elusive to define. It changed the pattern of that Sunday afternoon. My grandfather woke up with a snort and came into the living room with his hair still tousled from sleep, followed by my grandmother, crease marks from the pillow zigzagging across her cheek. Where was Pearl Harbour? And we looked it up in the atlas, frightened to discover that only the Pacific Ocean separated us from the war now.

At first I didn't associate the attack on Pearl Harbour with the Japanese people I had known all my life — and I never associated it with Sakaye. We were in Grade Six that year, and she sat in the desk behind me. That was the year she started to speak English and she was the one who started whispering to me during school. I can't remember now what we used to whisper about — but that isn't important. What was important was the fact that we had discovered that communication went deeper than words, and it wasn't so much what one said that mattered, as it was that you knew you liked each other, and this was being communicated — and we had known that since Grade One. But of all the Japanese girls, Sakaye was still the shyest. Perhaps that is why the teacher pretended he didn't notice us whispering, because he never got after me when I was talking to Sakaye.

But the rumours that followed December seventh made it clear that for many in Mission City the association of the attack with the Japanese living in the Fraser Valley was only too real. Where did all the money go that the Japanese had been making on their farms? Not to the trades people of Mission, that was sure. And what about the Hyakawas' son who had gone over to Japan last year? What business could he have over there? And then reports about the fishing boats on the West Coast began to drift into Mission — the fishermen had been charting the coastal waters in preparation for the invasion of B.C. Someone even discovered that the fresh straw carefully laid down between the rows of young strawberry plants pointed directly to the Mission bridge — and because we boasted one of the three bridges that crossed the Fraser River, we suddenly saw ourselves as a strategic location, infiltrated by the enemy, and a prime target for attack.

All this never made any difference between Sakaye and me, but the other Japanese youngsters in my class must have realized what was being said, because there was a change in their attitude. For one thing, they stopped huddling together in little groups and talking in Japanese. After Pearl Harbour,

I can't remember hearing Japanese spoken again, except for the occasional swear word — and that was just as likely to have come from the white youngsters. For another, they were much friendlier than they had been. Roy Hoshira started bringing enough jawbreakers from his brother's grocery store for all those who sat around him — not just for his Japanese friends. The girls were different, too. I think we had always liked the Japanese girls — Miss Buckley's ruler and the May pole dancing had achieved that in Grade Three — but until Pearl Harbour, they had remained quiet and inscrutable. Pearl Harbour never made any difference in my friendship with Sakaye, though, not even when people started saying that her uncle was an admiral of the Pacific Fleet. . . .

It must have been only a few weeks after Pearl Harbour that the Japanese woman came to our United Church for the morning service. The minister had already begun the short sermon he preached for the children before they went downstairs for Sunday School, and I was sitting in front of the church with the junior choir, facing the congregation. So we saw it all. The door opened quietly and Sakaye's mother walked in. In all the years I had been going to St. David's I had never seen any Japanese at our service. Furthermore, no one ever came to the church that late. She shuffled noiselessly down the aisle with a polite, half-apologetic smile, and slipped into the empty space beside Mrs. Hancock near the back of the church. I don't suppose many in the congregation even knew she was there. But the junior choir did — we saw it all —we saw Mrs. Hancock turn to look at her, and we heard Mrs. Hancock sniff. And we saw Mrs. Hancock rise self-righteously and walk out of the pew leading her daughters to a place nearer the front of the church. Only Mrs. Grimsby kept her seat in the pew as one by one the others followed Mrs. Hancock's example. Mrs. Grimsby was strangely lost without her Legion Auxiliary uniform, and although we recognized her expression as the one which followed Miss Buckley's ruler episodes, it was useless without a piano on which to thump *"come* lasses and lads", and she couldn't rally us as she might have. So she sat erect, trying to people the empty spaces in the pew between her and Sakaye's mother at the other end with her will alone. The minister ended his sermon abruptly, and in a tired voice announced the hymn. When everyone else was singing "The Church's One Foundation", Sakaye's mother got up and walked out as quietly as she had come in — and I was suddenly reminded of flour sack petticoats and panties stitched with yarn. I guess the other kids were, too, because nobody in the junior choir sang that morning. Just nobody.

And nobody said anything when the junior choir filed out into the vestry and we hung up our surplices in the cupboard. The younger children who had been sitting in front of the church with their Sunday School teachers came bursting through the door and clattered to their places in the different sections of the big room. Mrs. Hancock's class were all members of the choir, and we sat silent on our benches as she eased herself carefully into her chair and opened her lesson book. Nobody answered when she said good morning to us. And nobody said anything when she asked who could say the Bible verse for the day from memory. We wouldn't even look at her. And when she began reading the lesson, we all just sat there, staring at the floor or looking out the window. It was Billy Hunter who started it, and I suppose it was the bravest thing he had ever done. I was sitting beside him, and I knew how scared he was, because there were splotches of sweat all over the cover of his Bible. Mrs. Hancock was still reading from the lesson when Billy swallowed a great mouthful of air and belched. "My Jesus, mercy," he said firmly, and looked at me. I caught on. And as Mrs. Hancock went on reading, I swallowed air and belched and said, "My Jesus, mercy." Then everyone caught on. Sometimes it was a solo; sometimes as many as three of us at a time belched and said "My Jesus, mercy." Some of the girls weren't too impressive, but the boys produced some beauties. We knew the other classes were looking at us, and we could hear their shocked giggles. But not one of us laughed. We just sat there, and every time Mrs. Hancock opened her mouth to speak, somebody belched, and we all said, "My Jesus, mercy."

That was a long time ago. I don't know what became of Billy Hunter or Mrs. Grimsby, and I don't know if Mrs. Hancock kept on teaching Sunday School, because I never went back. I never said anything about it to Sakaye — and then one morning when we got to school we found that all the Japanese youngsters were gone. My mother had been dead for two months when Sakaye's letter arrived, so there was no one to tell me that Sakaye had had to get permission from the Canadian authorities to write to me, and that her letter had been censored — and it was only a few years ago when I read about the Japanese internment that I realized how Sakaye must have waited for my reply.

I wish I could answer Sakaye's letter and tell her all this, because now I know that it was important after all. She must be nearly forty, and she may still be living someplace on the prairies.

But I can't read the address on her letter anymore.

Families

Jewish Christmas

Fredelle Bruser Maynard

Christmas, when I was young, was the season of bitterness. Lights beckoned and tinsel shone, store windows glowed with mysterious promise, but I knew the brilliance was not for me. Being Jewish, I had long grown accustomed to isolation and difference. Difference was in my bones and blood, and in the pattern of my separate life. My parents were conspicuously unlike other children's parents in our predominantly Norwegian community. Where my schoolmates were surrounded by blond giants appropriate to a village called Birch Hills, my family suggested still the Russian plains from which they had emigrated years before. My handsome father was a big man, but big without any suggestion of physical strength or agility; one could not imagine him at the wheel of a tractor. In a town that was all wheat and cattle, he seemed the one man wholly devoted to urban pursuits; he operated a general store. Instead of the native costume — overalls and mackinaws — he wore city suits and pearl-gray spats. In winter he was splendid in a plushy chinchilla coat with velvet collar, his black curly hair an extension of the high Astrakhan hat which he had brought from the Ukraine. I was proud of his good looks, and yet uneasy about their distinctly oriental flavor.

My mother's difference was of another sort. Her beauty was not so much foreign as timeless. My friends had slender young Scandinavian mothers, light of foot and blue of eye; my mother was short and heavyset, but with a face of classic proportions. Years later I found her in the portraits of Ingres and Corot — face a delicate oval, brown velvety eyes, brown silk hair centrally parted and drawn back in a lustrous coil — but in those days I saw only that she too was different. As for my grandparents, they were utterly unlike the benevolent, apple-cheeked characters who presided over happy families in my favorite stories. (Evidently all those happy families were gentile.) My grandmother had no fringed shawl, no steel-rimmed glasses. (She read, if at all, with the help of a magnifying glass from Woolworth's.) Ignorant, apparently, of her natural role as gentle occupant of the rocking chair, she was ignorant too of the world outside her apartment in remote Winnipeg. She had brought Odessa with her, and — on my rare visits — she smiled lovingly, uncomprehendingly, across an ocean of time and space. Even more unreal was my grandfather, a black cap and a long beard bent over the Talmud. I felt for him a kind of amused tenderness, but I was glad that my schoolmates could not see him.

At home we spoke another language — Yiddish or Russian — and ate rich foods whose spicy odors bore no resemblance to the neighbor's cooking. We did not go to church or belong to clubs or, it seemed, take any meaningful part in the life of the town. Our social roots went, not down into the foreign soil on which fate had deposited us, but outwards, in delicate, sensitive connections, to other Jewish families in other lonely prairie towns. Sundays, they congregated around our table, these strangers who were brothers; I saw that they too ate knishes and spoke with faintly foreign voices, but I could not feel for them or for their silent swarthy children the kinship I knew I owed to all those who had been, like us, both chosen and abandoned.

All year I walked in the shadow of difference; but at Christmas above all, I tasted it sour on my tongue. There was no room at the tree. "You have Hanukkah," my father reminded me. "That is *our* holiday." I knew the story, of course — how, over two thousand years ago, my people had triumphed over the enemies of their faith, and how a single jar of holy oil had miraculously burned eight days and nights in the temple of the Lord. I thought of my father lighting each night another candle in the *menorah,* my mother and I beside him as he recited the ancient prayer: "Blessed art Thou, O Lord our God, ruler of the universe, who has sanctified us by thy commandments and commanded us to kindle the light of Hanukkah." Yes, we had our miracle too. But how could it stand against the glamor of Christmas: What was *gelt,* the traditional gift coins, to a sled packed with surprises? What was Judas Maccabaeus the liberator compared with the Christ child in the manger? To my sense of exclusion was added a sense of shame. "You *killed* Christ!" said the boys on the playground. "*You* killed him!" I knew none of the facts behind this awful accusation, but I was afraid to ask. I was even afraid to raise my voice in the chorus of "Come All Ye Faithful" lest I be struck down for my unfaithfulness by my own God, the wrathful Jehovah. With all the passion of my child's heart I longed for a younger, more compassionate deity with flowing robe and silken hair. Reluctant conscript to a doomed army, I longed to change sides. I longed for Christmas.

Although my father was in all things else the soul of indulgence, in this one matter he stood firm as Moses. "You cannot have a tree, *herzele.* You shouldn't even want to sing the carols. You are a Jew." I turned the words over in my mind and on my tongue. What was it, to be a Jew in Birch Hills, Saskatchewan? Though my father spoke of Jewishness as a special distinction, as far as I could see it was an inheritance without a kingdom, a check on a bank that had failed. Being Jewish was mostly not doing things other people did — not eating pork, not going to Sunday school, not entering, even playfully, into childhood romances, because the only boys around were *goyishe* boys. I remember, when I was five or six, falling in love with Edward, Prince of Wales. Of the many arguments with which Mama might have dampened my ardor, she chose surely the most extraordinary. "You can't marry him. He isn't Jewish." And of course, finally, definitely, most crushing of all, being Jewish meant not celebrating Christ's birth. My parents allowed me to attend Christmas parties, but they made it clear that I must receive no gifts. How I envied the white and gold Norwegians! Their Lutheran church was not glamorous, but it was less frighteningly strange than the synagogue I had visited in Winnipeg, and in the Lutheran church, each December, joy came upon the midnight clear.

It was the Lutheran church and its annual concert which brought me closest to Christmas. Here there was always a tree, a jolly Santa Claus, and a program of songs and recitations. As the town's most accomplished elocutionist, I was regularly invited to perform. Usually my offering was comic or purely secular — *Santa's mistake, The Night Before Christmas,* a scene from *A Christmas Carol.* But I had also memorized for such occasions a sweetly pious narrative about the housewife who, blindly absorbed in cleaning her house for the Lord's arrival, turns away a beggar and finds she has rebuffed the Savior himself. Oddly enough, my recital of this vitally un-Jewish material gave my parents no pain. My father, indeed, kept in his safe-deposit box along with other valuables a letter in which the Lutheran minister spoke gratefully of my last Christmas performance. "Through her great gift, your little Freidele has led many to Jesus." Though Papa seemed untroubled by considerations of whether this was a proper role for a Jewish child, reciting *The Visit* made me profoundly uneasy. And I suppose it was this feeling, combined with a natural disinclination to stand unbidden at the feast, which led me, the year I was seven, to rebel.

We were baking in the steamy kitchen, my mother and I
— or rather she was baking while I watched, fascinated as
always, the miracle of the strudel. First, the warm ball of
dough, no larger than my mother's hand. Slap, punch, bang —
again and again she lifted the dough and smacked it down on
the board. Then came the moment I loved. Over the kitchen
table, obliterating its patterned oilcloth, came a damask cloth;
and over this in turn a cloud of flour. Beside it stood my
mother, her hair bound in muslin, her hands and arms
powdered with flour. She paused a moment. Then, like a
dancer about to execute a particularly difficult pirouette, she
tossed the dough high in the air, catching it with a little
stretching motion and tossing again until the ball was ball no
longer but an almost transparent rectangle. The strudel was as
large as the tablecloth now. *"Unter Freidele's vigele Ligt eyn
groys veys tsigele,"* she sang. "Under Freidele's little bed a
white goat lays his silken head." *"Tsigele iz geforen handlen
Rozinkes mit mandlen. . . ."* For some reason that song, with
its gay fantastic images of the white goat shopping for raisins
and almonds, always made me sad. But then my father swung
open the storm door and stood, stamping and jingling his
galoshes buckles, on the icy mat.

"Boris, look how you track in the snow!"

Already flakes and stars were turning into muddy puddles.
Still booted and icy-cheeked he swept us up — a kiss on the
back of Mama's neck, the only spot not dedicated to strudel,
and a hug for me.

"You know what? I have just now seen the preacher.
Reverend Pederson, he wants you should recite at the
Christmas concert."

I bent over the bowl of almonds and snapped the nut-
cracker.

"I should tell him it's alright, you'll speak a piece?"

No answer.

"Sweetheart — dear one — you'll do it?"

Suddenly the words burst out. "No, Papa! I don't want to!"

My father was astonished. "But why not? What is it with you?"

"I hate those concerts!" All at once my grievances swarmed up in an angry cloud. "I never have any fun! And everybody else gets presents and Santa Claus never calls out 'Freidele Bruser'! They all know I'm Jewish!"

Papa was incredulous. "But, little daughter, always you've had a good time! Presents! What presents? A bag of candy, an orange? Tell me, is there a child in town with such toys as you have? What should you want with Santa Claus?"

It was true. My friends had tin tea sets and dolls with sawdust bodies and crude celluloid smiles. I had an Eaton Beauty with real hair and delicate jointed body, two French dolls with rosy bisque faces and — new this last Hanukkah — Rachel, my baby doll. She was the marvel of the town: exquisite china head, overlarge and shaped like a real infant's, tiny wrinkled hands, legs convincingly bowed. I had a lace and taffeta doll bassinet, a handmade cradle, a full set of rattan doll furniture, a teddy bear from Germany and real porcelain dishes from England. What *did* I want with Santa Claus? I didn't know. I burst into tears.

Papa was frantic now. What was fame and the applause of the Lutherans compared to his child's tears? Still bundled in his overcoat he knelt on the kitchen floor and hugged me to him, rocking and crooning. "Don't cry, my child, don't cry. You don't want to go, you don't have to. I tell them you have a sore throat, you can't come."

"Boris, wait. Listen to me." For the first time since my outburst, Mama spoke. She laid down the rolling pin, draped the strudel dough delicately over the table, and wiped her hands on her apron. "What kind of a fuss? You go or you don't go, it's not such a big thing. But so close to Christmas you shouldn't let them down. The one time we sit with them in the church and such joy you give to them. Freidele, look at me.

. . ." I suffled loudly and obeyed, not without some satisfaction in the thought of the pathetic picture I made. "Go this one time, for my sake. You'll see, it won't be so bad. And if you don't like it — pffff, no more! All right? Now, come and help with the raisins."

On the night of the concert we gathered in the kitchen again, this time for the ritual of the bath. Papa set up the big tin tub on chairs next to the black iron stove. Then, while he heated pails of water and sloshed them into the tub, Mama set out my clothes. Everything about this moment contrived to make me feel pampered, special. I was lifted in and out of the steamy water, patted dry with thick towels, powdered from neck to toes with Mama's best scented talcum. Then came my "reciting outfit". My friends in Birch Hills had party dresses mail-ordered from Eaton's — crackly taffeta or shiny rayon satin weighted with lace or flounces, and worn with long white stockings drawn up over long woollen underwear. My dress was Mama's own composition, a poem in palest peach crepe de chine created from remants of her bridal trousseau. Simple and flounceless, it fell from my shoulders in a myriad of tiny pleats no wider than my thumbnail; on the low-slung sash hung a cluster of silk rosebuds. Regulation drop-seat underwear being unthinkable under such a costume, Mama had devised a snug little apricot chemise which made me, in a world of wool, feel excitingly naked.

When at last I stood on the church dais, the Chrismas tree glittering and shimmering behind me, it was with the familiar feeling of strangeness. I looked out over the audience-congregation, grateful for the myopia that made faces indistinguishable, and began:

A letter came on Christmas morn
In which the Lord did say
"Behold my star shines in the east
And I shall come today.
Make bright thy hearth. . . ."

The words tripped on without thought or effort. I knew by heart every nuance and gesture, down to the modest curtsey and the properly solemn pace with which I returned to my seat. There I huddled into the lining of Papa's coat, hardly hearing the "Beautiful, beautiful!" which accompanied his hug. For this was the dreaded moment. All around me, children twitched and whispered. Santa had come.

"Olaf Swenson!" Olaf tripped over a row of booted feet, leapt down the aisle and embraced an enormous package. "Ellen Njaa! Fern Dahl! Peter Bjorkstrom!" There was a regular procession now. All jubilant. Everywhere in the hall children laughed, shouted, rejoiced with their friends. "What'd you get?" "Look at mine!" In the seat next to me, Gunnar Olsen ripped through layers of tissue: "I got it! I got it!" His little sister wrestled with the contents of a red net stocking. A tin whistle rolled to my feet and I turned away, ignoring her breathless efforts to retrieve it.

And then — suddenly, incredibly, the miracle came. "Freidele Bruser!" For me, too, the star had shone. I looked up at my mother. A mistake surely. But she smiled and urged me to my feet. "Go on, look, he calls you!" It was true. Santa was actually coming to meet me. My gift, I saw, was not wrapped — and it could be no mistake. It was a doll, a doll just like Rachel, but dressed in christening gown and cap. "Oh Mama, look! He's brought me a doll! A twin for Rachel! She's just the right size for Rachel's clothes. I can take them both for walks in the carriage. They can have matching outfits. . . ." I was in an ecstasy of plans.

Mama did not seem to be listening. She lifted the hem of the gown. "How do you like her dress? Look, see the petticoat?"

"They're beautiful" I hugged the doll rapturously. "Oh, Mama, I *love* her! I'm going to call her Ingrid. Ingrid and Rachel. . . ."

During the long walk home Mama was strangely quiet.

Usually I held my parents' hands and swung between them. But now I stepped carefully, clutching Ingrid.

"You had a good time, yes?" Papa's breath frosted the night.

"Mmmmmmmm."

I rubbed my warm cheek against Ingrid's cold one. "It was just like a real Christmas. I got the best present of anybody. Look, Papa — did you see Ingrid's funny little cross face? It's just like Rachel's. I can't wait to get her home and see them side by side in the crib."

In the front hall, I shook the snow from Ingrid's lace bonnet. "A hot cup cocoa maybe?" Papa was already taking the milk from the icebox. "No, no, I want to get the twins ready for bed!" I broke from my mother's embrace. The stairs seemed longer than usual. In my arms Ingrid was cold and still, a snow princess. I could dress her in Rachel's flannel gown, that would be the thing. . . . The dolls and animals watched glassy-eyed as I knelt by the cradle. It rocked at my touch, oddly light. I flung back the blankets. Empty. Of course.

Sitting on the cold floor, the doll heavy in my lap, I wept for Christmas. Nothing had changed then, after all. For Jews there was no Santa Claus, I understood that. But my parents. . . . *Why* had they dressed Rachel?

From the kitchen below came the mingled aromas of hot chocolate and buttery popcorn. My mother called softly. "Let them call," I said to Ingrid-Rachel. "I don't care!" The face of the Christmas doll was round and blank under her cap; her dress was wet with my tears. Brushing them away, I heard my father enter the room. He made no move to touch me or lift me up. I turned and saw his face tender and sad like that of a Chagall violinist. "Mama worked every night on the clothes," he said. "Yesterday even, knitting booties."

Stiff-fingered, trembling, I plucked at the sleeve of the christening gown. It was indeed a miracle — a wisp of batiste but as richly overlaid with embroidery as a coronation robe.

For the first time I examined Rachel's new clothes — the lace insets and lace overlays, the French knots and scalloped edges, the rows of hemstitching through which tiny ribbons ran like fairy silk. The petticoat was tucked and pleated. Even the little diaper showed an edge of hand crochet. There were booties and mittens and a ravishing cap.

"Freidele, dear one, my heart," my father whispered. "We did not think. We could not know. Mama dressed Rachel in the new clothes, you should be happy with the others. We so much love you."

Outside my window, where the Christmas snow lay deep and crisp and even, I heard the shouts of neighbors returning from the concert. "Joy to the world!" they sang,

> Let earth receive her king!
> Let every heart prepare Him room
> And heaven and nature sing . . .

It seemed to me, at that moment, that I too was a part of the song. I wrapped Rachel warmly in her shawl and took my father's hand.

Tante Tina's Lament
David Waltner-Toews

Hänschen is a fool
and I am his mother,
Lord forgive us both.
Hänschen struts about the city
like a chicken.
He wears a pink shirt
and plaid, big-bottomed hosen.
When he was little,
his bottom was like a zwieback,
I spanked his little bum
and how he crowed!

Now he wags his tongue at me
and thinks I am ignorant.
He says farmers have no brains
they should all be businessmen.
He says farm girls don't know how to walk
and I don't know how to barbecue a steak.
Oh his heart is full of borscht
and his words are sour.
Don't call me Hänschen, he says.
My name is John.
Do I not know my son's name?
Did I not argue for six nights
with David, my husband, about that name?

On Wednesday night
the young people go to church.
They eat platz and give testimonies.
The girls have long golden hair.
Their cheeks are rosy from harvest
and dresses cover their knees.
When the young people sing together
it is heaven above and earth below
with sopranos and basses.

But my Hänschen
goes to dance in the city.
He has a girl friend
She smears grease on her lips.
Her blond hair is cut and curled
and her knees are bare
like a young calf.
When they dance
their legs are noodles
and the music is a tractor.
The girl friend says it is not a shame
for a woman to cut her hair.

She thinks Mennonites are like Hutterites
and has never heard of roll kuchen.
What good can come of that?

Hänschen says she is a modern girl.
He says we must speak English to her
because she goes to the United Church.
He says Low German is a pile of manure.
Listen here, my little boy.
I will surround you with Low German.
I will speak piles of it to you.
Then you will know what Low German is!
Then you will remember —
a mother's anger is a willow switch.

He does not listen.
We are poor, he says.
We do not know how to make money.
He wants to be rich, like the English,
and save us all from Mannagruetze.
His heart is tight as a peppernut.
His head is a piroshki
stuffed with fruit.

In the barn, the cats eat mice
and wait for milking time.
When my man comes in
I serve him dinner, steaming on a plate.
But my son does not know happiness.

On New Year's Eve
we go to church at night,
and on Easter
as the sun rises
we sing praises.
Hänschen is at church by eleven
on Easter.

On New Year's Eve
he goes to dance.
He does not even come to hear the children
on Christmas Eve!
When he was still wet behind the ears
he was a wise man in the play.

Oh my son
my heart is heavy,
thick as glums.
If you come home
it will rise, light and sweet.
I will make you porzelky for breakfast
and we will celebrate the New Year
every morning.

A Mouthful of Tongue
Adele Wiseman

The winter my father went to Vancouver to look for a job, Joe
and I were still too young to go to school. We stayed home and
my mother found things for us to do after Belle and Arty left
the house. In those days the house was full of roomers. You'd
be surprised at how many tenants can be crowded into a five-
room bungalow, particularly if the landlady and her four
children are flexible about shifting around to accommodate the
guests. For Mrs. Lemon alone we had moved our belongings
in turn to every room in the house. Every time my mother gave
in and said, "All right, you come," we tried to clear out a room
other than the one that she had occupied last time, because my
mother wanted it to be a fresh start each time. She did not want
to remind Mrs. Lemon that last time she had moved out
because we were piping poison gas into her room.

Joe was still practically a baby. He missed my father

terribly. Everybody said so, and I could prove it any time. All I had to say was, "Where's Daddy? Daddy's gone away." Fat tears would glaze his trusting eyes; his belly would heave into some mysterious preparatory discipline, and from his mouth would burst the foghorn bass bellow that was the pride of our house. You couldn't bear to listen for long. Remorsefully, I would yell into his weeping, "He's coming! He's coming home!" Joe would hesitate uncertainly, the sobs clucking and gurgling. I completed the cure. "What'll he bring? What'll he bring me?" It was a pleasure to see the joy spread over his good-natured face. "What'll he bring Joe?"

"Me! Me!" chuckled Joe. I played nicely with him for a while after that.

Every morning I took a trip. Sometimes I took Joe. We had our route laid out. To a certain listing, brown-shingled house down the street we went, labouring through unshovelled snow. Up icy front steps we climbed, on all fours. Finally we stood rattling the doorknob and banging with our fists on the door. If no one came to the door I would stand back and let Joe holler into the sparkling air. That was when it was good to have him with me. "Mrs. Fi . . . fer!" His powerful roar shattered the air, scattering the billion tiny crystals that darted thick and glittering in the daylight and sending them blinking to hide in the snow. That brought Mrs. Fifer running.

Joe got his voice from an uncle on my father's side. That uncle was born with church bells in his chest. An aesthetic priest had gone mad over his voice and had pressed him into the service of the church choir, because there was no one in all Russia who could intone like he could, "Christ is risen!" Through three successive pogroms his voice had been the salvation of his entire family, and of everyone else who'd had the sense to seek refuge in his house. For when the parishioners ran amok they left his house religiously alone. "They respect me," he used to say, with not a little pride.

We all of us in our house had little characteristics that were passed on to us from relatives, some of whom we had never known, so that we grew up with the feeling that we were part of a much larger family than we actually had. They told me that I took after my aunt Yenta, my mother's sister, who lived only a few blocks away. It was because I talked too much. Yenta herself was always the first, though, to accuse me of spreading family secrets. Nobody ever told me why they weren't secrets until I talked about them. They were just things everybody in the house discussed. But the minute they found out I'd told Mrs. Fifer they became secrets.

Mrs. Fifer was an old lady. She and her husband lived in one of the ground-floor apartments in the ramshackle house right next door to the apartment of my aunt Yenta's best friend, Dvosieh Krotz. She was always wonderfully pleased to see me and Joe too, though he wasn't much to talk to yet. She loosed our clothing, unwound our scarves, and gave us cookies from a shredded-wheat box.

As we ate Mrs. Fifer would ask me all kinds of questions, and I would answer her while my index finger kept the turning crumbs poked back safely in my mouth. Mrs Fifer liked talking to me. She used to tell my mother what a nice little girl I was to come and visit, and how polite I was to spend time talking to an old lady. My mother always smiled in an apprehensive kind of way.

They were not only family things Mrs. Fifer asked about, with her intensely interested, kind old face bent forward to hear what I said. She took an interest in our roomers too, what they said, what they did, what my mother thought of them, did they pay their rent on time, which ones were on relief, did any of them have secret jobs the relief didn't know about, was it true this one had fought with that one over a pot on the stove, and so on. I loved to listen to the talk in our house, so I was particularly good at correcting Mrs. Fifer when she said, for instance, "And did your Daddy say so and so?"

"No, he said such and such," I would reply, proud to be able to set an adult straight.

How did my auntie always know what I'd been saying to

Mrs. Fifer? I could tell by preliminary stamping on the ice outside and by the way she slammed into our house, rattling the frosted windows, how serious her visit was going to be in its consequences for me. She would always call out before she was fully over the threshold, "I'm not staying. Don't make tea." She kicked off my uncle's old galoshes and came up the five hall steps, bringing the chill of the outdoors in the room with her. Joe, who sat with his flannel kimono loose, shuddered up and down his rolls of baby fat, accompanying his shudders with resonant, self-comforting growls.

"What?" cried my aunt, readily indignant, "is the child doing naked?"

"Don't come near him, auntie," I said, "Mama's fixing his combinations. We got the other ones wet outside."

"You," said my aunt, "Leubitchka with the active lips, does Mrs. Fifer know that too already? It hurts me for you Rivka," she turned to my mother. "This child has a faceful of mouth, a mouthful of tongue, a tongueful of every little thing that goes on in this house, so Mrs. Fifer can run and spread it like fire all over the prairie."

"Mrs. Fifer's sick," I said, "in an armchair, covered over. I was there with Joe."

"Not too sick to ask questions," said my aunt bitterly. "It hurts me, Rivka. . . ."

"It hurts me," like "I'm not staying, don't make tea," was one of those baffling statements that Yenta made. She always stayed. She always drank tea. And she never told you where she hurt. She always changed the subject in mid-sentence. "It hurts me your name should be dragged through the mud."

There was no mud any more. "Through the snow," I offered.

"What?" said my aunt.

"Nothing," I said. Maybe she meant "It hurts me your name should be dug to the mud." But why did it hurt? And how did a name get dragged or dug? Anyway, with her dark, flashing eyes and glowing skin, she never looked as though anything was hurting her.

"It's not Mrs. Fifer spreads the stories," said my mother quietly.

"Don't be foolish," said my aunt heatedly. "They fly by themselves, all over town?" She looked at me. "On wings of tongue they fly."

I laughed. I like the way my aunt talked. She laughed too. In spite of the things she called me we got along, and it sounded as though it might go easy with me and Mrs. Fifer today, though you never could tell. They laughed and laughed and suddenly they jumped you.

"Mama says Mrs. Fifer doesn't tell anything," I said, before I could stop myself.

"Oh she doesn't?" said my aunt. "So if your mother says she doesn't then she doesn't. Should I argue? When your mother gets stubborn I might as well talk to the walls." My aunt stopped talking.

My mother, smiling, looked up from her stitching. "How's your friend Dvosieh?"

My aunt ignored the question and addressed me directly. "Why do you talk so much? Where do you get your tongue? Why do you tell her everything?"

"She asks me," I faltered. "I take after you," I added quickly.

"Don't be disrespectful," said my mother.

"But you say so," I said.

"It's not what you say but when," explained my aunt, "that makes respect. Is it true then?" she continued, "what she told Mrs. Fifer? Are you taking Mrs. Lemon in again? As if you haven't got enough to worry about. Don't do it Rivka. What do you need her for? Tell her no for a change. Let her find somewhere else."

A Mouthful of Tongue   85

"She's here already," said my mother.

"In the house?" my aunt's voice disappeared suddenly in her lips.

"No, she had to report to the relief," said my mother. "But she moved in this morning."

My aunt frowned. Her eyes seemed to light on me.

"That's what I told Mrs. Fifer," I said.

My aunt shook her head. "She's getting worse, not better. One day she's fine, talks like anybody else; the next day suddenly, out of nowhere, an accusation you can't make sense of; then locks herself in her room, not a word; then starts to run around to the neighbours. Did you hear what happened? Yesterday she went to her husband's people again and made a scandal. She said they're keeping her husband locked up a prisoner in the TB hospital. She said they're paying the government to put germs in his X-rays to kill him. They wouldn't let her into the house so she went shouting up and down their fancy street."

"It must be very embarrassing for them," my mother said. "The rich are so sensitive."

"Its hurts me for them," said my aunt in a surprisingly satisfied voice for one in pain. "They didn't even offer her a glass of tea, not a bite. They tried to give her money to go away, five dollars to ease her pain. She threw it at them. And they from behind closed doors, afraid to let her in, a human being like themselves. She didn't have a mouthful of saliva to chew on all day. She walked from their place to the Hudson's Bay Company in the snow, and fainted twice, once in the notions and the second time when they took her to the restroom. So strangers called an ambulance and took her to the hospital. It's all over town."

"I know," said my mother. "An ambulance brought her this morning."

My aunt laughed. "She certainly gets free public transportation. It's always ambulances and police cars." My aunt could never quite overcome the suspicion that it was somehow useful to Mrs. Lemon to be sick. In spite of her hard talk Yenta had taken Mrs. Lemon into her own house three disastrous times already. Things always started off well enough, with my aunt proud of how well she could handle a problem that had once again vanquished my mother, and Mrs. Lemon temporarily tranquil because she had once again fought off some obscure threat. Then my auntie's crony, Dvosieh Krotz, would come over to sit in and give advice, the same crony who lived behind the wall of Mrs. Fifer's flat.

Dvosieh advised friendship and reason, and the sane discussion of past delusions in the calm of present clarity. My aunt showed her friendship through the simple means of frequent reiteration. "I say to her," she would explain to my mother, "You see, I'm your friend, Mrs. Krotz is your friend. We're all your friends." And Yenta was not one to be stingy with her sympathy. "Your poor husband, where is this 'san'? Up north? What's up north? The Eskimos! Why would they put a TB san up north? So they can cure him of consumption and kill him with pneumonia?"

Under the stress of reason, advice and friendship, Mrs. Lemon's suspicions were rapidly forced, like monstrous bulbs, in her mind's darkness. By some inspired stroke of malignancy her fits always crystallized around Yenta's most sensitive spot. My aunt is a wonderful cook and a proud one, justly famed in our neighbourhood. Mrs. Lemon always ended up by accusing her of poisoning her food. My aunt could not resist taking it personally. She would become incensed and run among the neighbours herself. When my mother tried to reason with her she grew even more irate, "See here Rivka, listen here. You say it's madness, for everybody. Has she ever told you you poison her food? No!"

"But I've gassed her and drugged her and I whisper in her room at night," my mother defended herself.

"That doesn't make any difference. Three times she's lived

in my house and three times I've poisoned her. It's too much. If at least once I'd gassed her I wouldn't feel so much she was deliberately needling me. She means something by it."

"She's sick," sighed my mother.

"You always find something good to say for everybody," sniffed Yenta.

This time, however, my aunt had a more serious threat to disclose against Mrs. Lemon than her own erratic ire. After this last scandal in the south end the in-laws had sworn, in front of witnesses, that if it happened once more, if once more she made trouble, they would have her put away.

"They wouldn't," said my mother after a silence. "She's harmless."

"Oh yes they would," said my aunt. "They're out of all patience. Once more and they'll put her away for good. They don't like scandals on the south side."

"You make money you lose patience," said my mother.

"Where will they put her away?" I asked.

My mother and my aunt looked at each other. "Nowhere," said my mother hastily.

"Mrs. Fifer hasn't got a radio," I was happy to contribute.

My mother sighed. "Just don't repeat everything we've said to Mrs. Lemon."

"All right," I said. "I like Mrs. Lemon," I added. "Joe and I don't want them to put her away. Nor Belle nor Arty neither."

"Just don't talk," said Yenta quickly, " and they won't."

"She's like you, Yenta," my mother remarked.

"Like me? How like me? I'm no child. A child shouldn't sell your teeth every time you open your mouth."

This was not the first time I had heard that "they" could do something dreadful to Mrs. Lemon. No wonder she had fits. I could not separate the idea of Mrs. Lemon's being "put away for good" from the memory of the time our dog Rhubarb had to be put away, and the man had come with a closed wagon with a grilled door in back to take her away, and she had stood still behind the grille, and had left us all standing and watching and stained forever with her mute, despairing eyes. Just let them try to come and get Mrs. Lemon.

Mrs. Lemon played with us, not the way most adults do, always with the end of the game in sight, as though telling themselves approvingly over their impatience, "now we are playing with the children for a little while." Rather, she let us play with her. Quietly she sat or stood or turned as we directed her, never imitating us and never rushing us through her time. We usually played in the kitchen those winter afternoons. Sometimes we played in her room, but my mother didn't like that. She said that if Mrs. Lemon saw that we kept strictly away from her room there would be less chance of upsetting her. So it was mostly in the kitchen that we had our games, the warm white kitchen with its frost-fuzzed windows, its big grey electric stove, its knife-scarred wooden table covered by a knife-scarred printed oilcloth, and its wooden rung chairs, behind which Mrs. Lemon allowed herself to be barricaded while Joe and I pretended we had captured her and had her in our power. She stood quietly, occasionally saying something nice in reply to my mother, like "No, they're not bothering me."

I liked the way Mrs. Lemon looked. She made me think. She didn't look like a lemon. She was thin and brown. Her hair was black and rolled round and round at the back of her head. Her eyes were big and bugged out a little, with dark brown middles and yellowish white parts. And she was extra brown all around the eyes.

In spite of my mother's instructions Joe and I were not strangers in Mrs. Lemon's room. We knew her few belongings well, especially the raddled orange fur collar with the fox's head and its loosely snapping jaw. On her bureau sat a little brown old-country picture of her mother, her father, and two sturdy boys, with a little, big-eyed girl between them I knew was Mrs. Lemon long ago. I always wanted to ask her which one was the brother who had dropped dead when they were burying her father; right into the grave he dropped. I knew all about what a sad life she had had that made her go funny sometimes. But I never did. There was another picture, in a small frame, of Mr. Lemon. He wore a white collar and looked bristly, and I said like my mother did when she mentioned him sometimes, "He'll get well soon," in the same confident voice that pleased Mrs. Lemon. The candy was in an almost empty top right-hand drawer, in a box with a gypsy on it.

Sometimes she would say, "Do you want to take a walk with me?" And my mother would say, "Mrs. Lemon, you shouldn't, they're too wild." And she would beg and make promises along with us until my mother said, "All right, but you mustn't buy them anything." And Mrs. Lemon wouldn't say anything and my mother would bite her lip, for fear she had hurt Mrs. Lemon's feelings by implying she couldn't afford to spend her relief tickets on us.

They would truss us up and we would move stiffly off between the snowbanks. I slithered around on Arty's old moccasins and screamed into Joe, knocking him over like a kewpie doll, sideways, into the piled-up snow, where he lay, one arm standing straight out, the other buried. His cries shattered the still, needle-charged air. Mrs. Lemon dug him out, soothed him, called him "little snowman", and I magnanimously let him push me back, which he did, chuckling his deep bass chuckle. I flung myself, screaming, into the bank, and waited for a panting Mrs. Lemon to right me before I flung myself on Joe again. We were snow plastered and steaming through every layer by the time we reached the corner grocery. Inside it was hot and dingy and glamorous. We consulted with Mrs. Lemon for a long time and then she bought us each a string of pink and white crystallized sugar and a flat square package of bubble gum with a hockey picture in it that Arty would be nice for.

"I'm not giving Arty my hockey picture," I suggested to Joe. Joe gripped his with his mitt against his chest and shook his head fiercely, eyes shining, cheeks fiery, nose running. But I knew very well he would rush, the minute Arty made his noisy, dishevelled entrance from school, with his hockey picture extended, for the immediate gratification of a big brother's thanks. Arty wouldn't win mine so easily. I knew the subtler pleasures of the drawn-out wooing and the gradual surrender. "I have one too, Arty, see? No you can't. What'll you give me? Can I play in your igloo?"

So the winter passed. One day, late in February, my mother was sitting alone in the kitchen, sewing and humming to herself. Mrs. Lemon slipped in so quietly my mother didn't even hear her, till the hissing whisper started her out of her chair. "Do you think I don't know why you're singing? But you won't get me that easily." My mother got up and made some tea, which they drank in utter silence. After that, Mrs. Lemon stopped talking almost entirely. Sometimes she sat in the kitchen without speaking for hours at a time, while my mother did her work, occasionally throwing her an anxious glance. At other times Mrs. Lemon stayed in her room. My mother warned us to leave her alone, then, and I heard her tell my sister that maybe if we just kept still too it would blow over.

One day she left the house very early. She spent the whole day wandering among the neighbours and talking to people about her suspicions. My mother knew what she was doing, as she had often received such confidences when Mrs. Lemon was living elsewhere. "Maybe she'll just talk it out of her system."

"No." My aunt was triumphantly certain. "There'll be trouble."

Mrs. Lemon returned home that evening, thoroughly chilled, blue tints frozen into her swarthy skin, and for the next few days she lay coughing in bed. My mother tended to her, talking gently and soothingly, and pretended she didn't notice that she got no answer.

"Maybe the fever will burn it away," said my mother hopefully.

"No," said my aunt, "I tell you Rivka, you won't avoid a scandal. And this time. . . ."

"I'll try to keep her in the house till it blows over," said my mother.

The coughing ceased and my mother listened anxiously to the silence. She sighed more frequently as she listened, and raised her hand often from her sewing to run it through her softly waving black hair.

Then one day Mrs. Lemon, who must have been waiting behind her door for a long time, took advantage of a moment when my mother had gone into her bedroom to slip out of her room, through the kitchen, down the hall steps and out the side door. Joe and I were playing on the kitchen floor and we called out to her, but she didn't seem to hear our pleased hellos; she was all dug down into her coat. Only the fox winked and snapped at us from her back as she bounded down the steps.

My mother ran out of our bedroom, but too late she scratched at the ice of the window. "What was she wearing? Was she dressed warmly?"

"Her winter coat and her live fox," I said. My mother still looked worried. She looked more worried as the day wore on. She talked to my sister in a low voice when Belle and Arty got home from school, and my sister looked worried too. I hung around them and looked worried too, and asked questions that touched on raw worry and was hushed up.

We were eating supper when Mrs. Lemon returned. She rushed up the stairs and through the kitchen to her room, still hunched in her coat, and I called after her, but again there was no reply, and my mother shushed me up.

We were still around the table when my aunt came stamping in. She came up the stairs with her coat still buttoned and a very excited expression on her face. "Is she in?" she nodded in the direction of Mrs. Lemon's room, and formed the words through almost silent lips.

My mother nodded.

"You'll have visitors tomorrow," said Yenta softly, and nodded toward Mrs. Lemon's room again. "Didn't I warn you?" My aunt undid her coat but remained planted in my uncle's old galoshes in the kitchen doorway. "She went there again, threw herself down into the snow on their lawn, made a big outline, it's still there, for all the neighbours to see, made a scene. . . ."

"She'll catch cold again," murmured my mother.

"She'll be well taken care of," said my aunt grimly. She paused and looked anxiously toward Mrs. Lemon's room and we all listened with her. "So . . . that's it. Maybe it's better this way Rivka, though . . . you know . . . somehow . . . it hurts me . . ."

"It hurts me too," said mother softly, staring down at Joe's plate. "It hurts me too."

The next morning I fought against going out of the house, though a part of me wanted to go and talk to Mrs. Fifer. I felt funny-bad all over, and I could tell that my mother felt badly too, though she insisted on sending us out for our fresh air until she realized that there was a blizzard blowing up. I whined about after her all morning, and Joe growled after me. It was out of his range to whine.

By early afternoon the snow was whipping past the windows and piling up against the fences and walls and making spooky sounds all around the house. We had to turn the lights on. Mama began to worry about the children who were at school. I told her not to worry about any little blizzard bothering Arty and Belle.

Suddenly, Mrs. Lemon made her appearance in the kitchen. She looked around quickly and without saying anything went to stand at the kitchen window, looking out to where you could see nothing but swirling snow. My mother was looking at her.

"Joe," I jumped up. "Let's capture Mrs. Lemon!"

Delighted, Joe slid off his chair and began to push it toward her, while I began to push my own. "You're our prisoner!" I shouted out, and rushed to pull another chair to her side. "Prisoner!" repeated Joe in organ tones.

"Children!" said my mother.

Mrs. Lemon had turned from the window and stood looking at us from behind the chairs.

"Children," said my mother again. "Come here!" She had risen.

I looked from her to Mrs. Lemon. "She'll be our prisoner," I cried. "Then they can't put her away!"

"Leuba!" cried my mother, in a terrible voice.

I started to cry. "We don't want them to send Mrs. Lemon away!"

At the word "away", Joe cut loose like a trained bullfrog. "Gone away!" he bellowed eyes closed, mouth enormous, comprehending in its quivering pink cavern the whole reverberating enormity of deprival. Unable to compete with his mighty gust of expression I contented myself with short, breathy, gasping whimpers and siren whines.

"Children!" my mother implored, "children!" We pitched on fervently. "Away!" I prompted as Joe paused for breath. Instantly he exhaled his heartbreak in a fresh gust of shattering sound.

"Children!" my mother's hands were at her ears. "Children! Children!"

"Children," said Mrs. Lemon suddenly, from behind her barricade. "Children," she said in a dazed voice.

I stopped in mid-note, amazed at the first sound I had heard Mrs. Lemon utter in days. Joe, unaware of all else but his art, bellowed on. Confused, I forgot how to turn him off. "Joe," I yelled. He redoubled his efforts. His face had turned a fierce red that extended all down his neck. My mother, alarmed, started to pat him lightly on the back, murmuring, "Yosele, what's the matter? Yosele."

"Shut up!" I yelled, right into Joe's open mouth, so

suddenly that he made a gulp and clicking sound and a little "whirrr", as though his spring had snapped, and he remained voiceless, staring at me with the big, wounded, swimming eyes of one utterly betrayed.

"Leuba!" cried Mrs. Lemon, and for the first time ever, other than to help me across the street or to put on my overthings she laid her hand on me. She had me gently by the shoulder and her voice was dazed and shocked and urgent. "Never say that to your brother. Never, never say that to your brother."

I had an awful feeling inside of me, as though I had swallowed a big stone. I started to cry, this time soft, painful tears that wouldn't make a noise but only little groans inside of me. "I only meant," I said to Joe, who was also streaming big, sighing tears, "I only meant, Daddy's coming, honest Joe, he's coming soon," I bawled. My mother held and rocked us both.

"They miss their father," said Mrs. Lemon. "Poor children, they miss their father."

By the time my aunt arrived, all puffy and snowed over, Mrs. Lemon was sitting with Joe on her lap, playing tickle with him and receiving raucous response. No blizzard has ever prevented my aunt from just dropping by at the crucial moment of a crisis, and from sitting with her lips all pursed up and her eyes fixed on one or other of us, with an accusing or anticipatory stare. Only this time she quickly became aware that something was amiss. Yenta's glance shot questioningly back and forth from my mother to Mrs. Lemon. What had happened? My aunt looked almost indignant. Had Mrs. Lemon gone crazy all of a sudden?

"It's a nice blizzard," said my mother, looking at her. "If only people who have far to go would have the sense to stay home."

"Troublemakers should always stay home," said my aunt, and smiled at Mrs. Lemon in the friendliest way.

Suddenly, three more people were huffing and puffing up

the stairs into the kitchen, all in enormous, snowed-over coats, all standing and making cold noises and throwing chills around while my mother and aunt helped them off with their overthings, all apologizing because they were dripping on the kitchen floor, as the hall was too small to hold them. Mrs. Lemon went and got a chair from her room and my aunt brought another from our room and my mother took her sewing off another chair and pretty soon they were all sitting and blowing on their knuckles and talking about how cold it was and my mother had a fresh kettle on.

Joe had offered himself genially back to Mrs. Lemon's arms, and he now sat at princely ease, staring at the visitors from astride her knee. Mrs. Lemon started to demonstrate my brother's extraordinary vocal endowments to the newcomers by tickling his belly. The strangers were struck dumb with admiration.

Then the men started to explain how hard it was to drive in a snowstorm, and how they had started out long ago and had stalled twice along the way. The heavy woman who had come with them sat gingerly on her seat and looked all around and finally up and down over her black beads at my aunt, who wore my uncle's old red woolen socks over her shoes, and pulled right up under her skirt, because my uncle is a tall man, with her bloomers tucked into them. They had big yellow and blue darns on them, beautifully sewn, because my aunt is a perfectionist. The lady coughed as she looked, and my aunt spread her knees further apart to give herself purchase, leaned slightly forward, straight of back, folded her arms across her chest, and stared back, with pursed lips and a coldly ironic eye. My aunt is a handsome woman, with a haughty face and thick, straight black hair. She was not going to be stared down on account of her socks.

One of the men, smallish, with a glistening stone in his tie that looked as though it would melt any minute, leaned from his chair and whispered, hesitantly but loudly enough for me to hear, to the beaded lady, "Er . . . which one?" The beaded lady then introduced Mrs. Lemon as her sister-in-law, and all kinds of cross-introductions were made. I stared at her. This was the enemy, on whose lawns the scandals were enacted, who never even offered a glass of tea, though my mother even now was pouring hers.

I cannot remember in detail exactly what was said during the next little while, but I do remember that I behaved very badly. The kitchen gradually filled and filled and stretched outward with sound, much of it coming from my lips. Numerous faces all turned toward me, with varying expressions of amazement, distaste, disapproval, despair, as I talked, interrupted, contradicted and mimicked. The rich lady coughed at the smoke from cigarettes the men had lit, which was mingling with the steam from the kettle to fog up the room. She took noisier and noisier breaths. My aunt told her very kindly that she hoped her brother's ailment didn't run in the family, which made her cough so hard her beads rattled. I started to cough too, and my brother Joe chuckled approvingly at me, adding a stentorian spur to my antics. He thought it was a fine game. My mother pleaded with me in a shocked voice to be quiet, please. I couldn't. I no longer knew how.

Then my aunt and the rich relative got into what seemed to be a traitorously amiable conversation about what an unmanageably talkative child I was, and my aunt told her how I couldn't keep family secrets, and I remember being fiercely hurt that she should sell a family secret of such magnitude to an enemy, and in front of strangers.

Finally, my mother ordered me out of the room and I stood there bawling and insisted that I wouldn't go unless Mrs. Lemon came with me. By this time she was the only true ally I had left in the world and I could not leave her to treachery. My last-ditch tantrum was interrupted by loud noises at the door. My brother Arty and my sister Belle were outside quarrelling about who would get into the house first, Belle, with both arms book-laden, with snowpants under her thick coat, besparkled and dishevelled, and chubby Arty, in breeches and high boots and fur-lined jacket, banging his hockey stick against the wall of the house and lashing icicles from the eaves as he argued. There wasn't room for both to squeeze in at once, so meanwhile they held the door open and the blast whipped up blue around the fogged-up kitchen, and everybody shivered.

"I don't care if you are a lady," challenged Arty, who had wedged his hockey stick in front of Belle so that it suddenly appeared in the kitchen doorway with an ancient pair of razor-sharp skates hanging from knotted yellow laces over its edge.

"Belle! Arty!" boomed Joe joyously, as the skates narrowly grazed his skull. The three strangers exchanged glances as the stick and swinging skates advanced into the kitchen, the blades blinking ferociously and slashing indiscriminately through the air.

"Arty!" cried my mother aghast. "Belle, shut the door for goodness sake! We have guests!" she added hopefully.

"I can't," wailed my sister. "He won't let me in."

"Arty, take your skates away!" cried my mother, as the wind howled around the kitchen.

The guests broke for the bedroom. They found their coats. There was confusion in the kitchen for the next few moments, with Belle and Arty getting out of their wet clothes and the guests trying to get into theirs, and everybody exchanging polite "goodbyes" and "come agains" and the beaded lady saying something about "in good hands", and the small man with the pin saying something about "family atmosphere", as he nodded his way vigorously to the hall. Then they left. Soon afterwards my aunt left, having just remembered she had a word to say to her friend Dvosieh down the street. Mrs. Lemon said she was tired, suddenly, she didn't know why, and retired to the quiet of her room.

"What happened?" asked my sister.

"She feels better," said my mother.

Joe deserted us to go and look at Arty's sled with him in the cellar. Belle and my mother started doing the dishes. My mother said she was afraid supper might be a little late tonight. Everything was flat and quiet suddenly. I picked up the crumbs on the table. "What can I do?" I asked. My mother came to the table and stood looking down at me. She looked lovely, with her long, fine nose, her delicate skin all pink, her deepset eyes shining golden brown. "Aren't you tired?" she asked, as though she really thought I might be, so early.

"No. Can I help you?"

"You know," said my mother, "the way you behaved . . ." Suddenly, unaccountably, she grabbed me up, so violently that my curls bounced over my eyes. "You've helped enough," she said into my ear, and it felt, from the way her stomach was shaking and from the muffled sounds she was making in my hair, as though she was laughing.

Petite Misère
Gabrielle Roy

Shortly after I came into the world, my father, because I was of frail health or because he himself — then old and sick had too great a pity for life, dubbed me "Petite Misère" — "Little Miss Misery". Even when stroking my hair, he used the name affectionately. It annoyed me and made me unhappy, as though it foreordained me, because of him, to suffering, I bridled and said within myself, "Oh no! I am not misery. Never shall I be like you!"

But one day he hurled the hateful name at me in anger. I don't even know any longer what can have deserved such an explosion; probably some mere trifle; my father went through long periods of dark moodiness, when he lacked all patience and seemed overwhelmed with regrets — perhaps also with too heavy responsibilities. Then, from time to time, a mere peal of laughter, breaking in upon him, penetrating him in the midst of his somber thoughts, aroused in him an outburst of irritation. Later on I understood that, constantly fearing for us both the least and the worst of evils, he especially wanted to put us early on guard against too great a yearning for happiness.

His distorted features, on this particular occasion, had seemed terrifying to me. He threatened me with his upraised hand; but, powerless to make up his mind to strike me, he hurled at me as an everlasting reproach: "Oh! Why did I ever have any children!"

Parents may think that such words, well beyond the understanding of children, do them no harm; but precisely because they are only half intelligible to them, children ponder them and make of them a torture.

I fled; I ran up to my attic, where, face against the floor, I tore my nails over the rough boards and tried to dig my way into them that I might die. Pressing my nose and mouth against their wood, I attempted to prevent myself from breathing. I believed that one could stop breathing at will, and thus leave evil behind, whenever one wants to, because it is evil.

Hours passed, and I turned over on my back; my face-down position was really too uncomfortable.

And then, through the attic window, which was just in my line of vision, I beheld the sky. It was a windy June day . . . and very handsome, very white clouds began to pass before my eyes. It seemed to me that the clouds were displaying themselves for my sole benefit. Over the roof, so close to me, the wind whistled. Even at that age I loved the wind in high places, attacking neither men nor trees, doing no harm, a simple traveler who whistles as he goes. Two large elms planted by my father thrust their highest branches to the edge of my window; by stretching my neck a little, I could watch them sway; and that, too, must have been for me alone, since I was the only person perched high enough to espy the upper branches of our elms.

Then, more than ever, I wanted to die, because of the emotion that a mere tree was able to arouse in me . . . sweet, traitorous emotion, revealing to me that sorrow has eyes the better to see how lovely is this world!

For a moment my attention was wholly enthralled by the sight of a spider lowering itself toward me from a ceiling rafter, at the tip of its silken path. Because of it, I forgot to cry. But strengthened by having eluded me for a few moments, my sorrow returned and filled all my soul, while at the same time I studied through my tears this poor, tiny insect life, which I could cut short with a tap of my finger.

And I said to myself: "My father wanted no part of me. No one wanted any part of me. I should not have come into the world." (Occasionally I had heard my mother referring to some poor woman already burdened with children and in ill health, who had just brought another into the world, remark with a sigh, "It's hard, but that is duty. What can you do? She certainly must do her duty!") That day I dug the word from my memories, seized upon it, and, not yet aware of the terrible meaning it contained, I repeated to myself, "A child of duty! I am a child of duty!" And the very sound of this word sufficed to make me weep anew, for sorrows I did not yet know.

Then I rediscovered the blue sky, sailing past the window. Why did the sky seem to me so beautiful that evening that never since, in any portion of the world, have I seen any like it? Was it because it was so indifferent toward me, who looked upon it?

As I was about to begin weeping once more, I heard steps resound along the hall on the second floor, beneath my attic. Then the door at the foot of the stairs opened. A voice — my mother's voice — called out: "The table is set; supper is ready. Enough sulking — come eat."

Despite everything, I was hungry, and that very fact, the shame of being tempted by food in the midst of my sorrow, made me deny my hunger and assert that I could not eat, that I never should be able to eat again.

At the foot of the stairs my mother said to me, "Well, if you want to sulk, sulk . . . but later on you won't find anything left to eat."

And she moved away with a resilient, still-youthful step.

Later my brother came to the foot of the stairs to cry out to me that he was going fishing in the little river . . . would I go with him? . . . make up my mind! He was not referring to the Red, our valley's important river, but to our small Seine, a narrow watercourse that twisted its way onward like a snake between thickets filled with rose haws, a tiny river buried in the grass, muddy, secret, of little danger to us, even were we to plunge into it headfirst . . . my pretty river, green as cats' eyes!

It was very difficult for me to resist, but once again the idea of joy being possible in a life corrupt with sorrow made me rebuff my brother and cry out that I wanted to be alone.

He also moved away at a rapid pace; I heard him trot down the length of the hall and then gallop down the main stairs leading to the lower floor of the house.

Then there was silence.

Later still the little Gauthiers, my cherished playmates, all three perched on their plank fence which separated our two properties — though I do recall there was also a vague field between them — kept calling me for a long while. As was our custom, they intoned their summonses to the bird tune of "Fred - er - ick - hast - thou - seen - me". But at exactly the same time, the bird itself was likewise singing. I had to make a real effort to distinguish between its brief phrase of song and the chanting of my friends: "Chris - tine - will - you - come - and - play? At - store - keep - ing - come - and - play: At - bear - train - ing - come - and - play?" At last they varied their recitative a bit; because this was the game I liked the best and because by this means they hoped they might coax me out of the house, they called out plainly, "Come and let's play funerals."

With that, I could not master the desire to look at them; I drew close to the edge of the window, and I saw them below, all three in a row on the high fence. Yet suddenly reflecting that they were children better loved by their parents than I was by mine, I quickly ducked my head before they could discover me, since, in an obstinate effort to find me, their small faces were scanning all the windows of our house. I turned around, lay down on my back, and stared at the dismal ceiling.

For a good while longer, without catching a glimpse of me, anywhere, the dear children called me, in all their youthful despair at seeing so fine a summer evening lost for play. They were still calling me when it was almost dark. Their mother told them to come in and go to bed. I heard their protests and then their mother's insistent voice. But before giving me up, the three of them lined up on the fence, cried out very loud, and with how deep a regret: "Good - night - Chris - ti - ne! Are - you - dead - Chris - tine? So - long - Chris - ti - nette!"

Now in the attic window the sky was dark. And my sorrow was reborn, but far more mysterious and unknown. I felt as though it were the future — the whole, long, terrible future of a child — that weighed upon me . . . and I cried in broken sobs, without knowing exactly why. Perhaps because I sensed within me, as among adults, enough cowardice to resign myself to life as it is . . . and perhaps life held me even more firmly in its grasp through curiosity.

I could still hear on the floors below certain sounds that informed me of the goings and comings in the house. Doors slammed. On the porch and then on our narrow cement part I heard my mother's footsteps, in her new shoes. True, this evening she was supposed to play cards at some friends'. She was in a hurry; her feet seemed to run . . . and I was miserable that — this evening — she could leave with a free heart to indulge herself in anything so futile as card playing.

The night seemed to rise toward me from the dark floors below. The big house was now wholly silent . . . maybe empty. . . . And my sorrow was beyond bearing, abandoned by all save by myself, save by my solitary concern — far too young, far too weak to understand that sorrow; and without any longer knowing its cause, I wept for sorrow itself, which is perhaps no more than a child alone.

Then my ear close to the floor heard the dragging, the overburdened tread of my father.

Gently he pulled open the door at the foot of the stairs. There he remained for a long while, without speaking. Perhaps he thought that I did not know he was standing with one foot raised to take the first step. But I could here his breathing . . . and maybe he could hear mine, so poignant was the silence between us.

At last he called out: "Little one! Petite Misère!"

Oh, how my throat tightened! Never after did I ever feel such a knot, drawn tight to the point of choking me. And it is possibly a good thing while very young to have suffered a terrible sorrow, for afterward sorrow no longer has the power really to astound us.

My old father tried again: "Child!"

Then, since I still gave no answer, my father said to me, "You must be hungry."

And later on, after another silence, he said to me, so sadly that even today, finding its way amid memories as crowded as a forest, the exact tone of my father's voice comes back to me: "I've made a rhubarb pie. . . . It's still hot. . . . Would you like to eat some?"

It's beyond me! Ever since that day, rhubarb pie has never tempted me; but before then, it seems I adored it, even though I was sick every time I ate any. That was why my mother made it only very rarely, and when — rarely — she served one, she would forbid me to take more than one tiny little piece. So, then, my father must have taken advantage of my mother's being out that evening . . . and I could see him rolling up his sleeves, searching for the flour, for the lard — never, indeed, could he succeed in laying his hand on anything around the house — lighting the stove, keeping an eye on the pie as it baked. . . . How could I have uttered an answer! What was the sorrow that all evening had kept me from my usual games compared to the sorrow which now held me in its grip! Was it then the same with sorrow as with the mysterious paths in my book of the *Thousand and One Nights,* where each led on to a broader avenue and disclosed ever-widening vistas?

I heard my father sigh. So slowly did he close the door that I barely was aware of the click of the latch. He went away.

Those slow, disheartened footsteps!

And yet I waited a few minutes, a long time it seemed to me. Then I smoothed out my wrinkled clothes. I patted my cheeks to remove the marks of my tears; and with the hem of my dress I tried to repair the smudges thus left on my face.

I went down, stopping at each step.

The table in our large kitchen was laid as though for a feast . . . a very sorry feast, for on the white cloth there was placed, at the center, only the pie, and at either end, far removed from each other, our two plates.

We took our places, my father and I, without having as yet exchanged so much as a glance.

Then my father pushed toward me the pie he had cut beforehand into such huge pieces that abruptly I burst into fresh tears. But at the same time I began to taste it.

Often during halts on his rough trips through lands being opened to colonization, when he had gone to settle immigrants there, my father had improvised his own meals over glowing embers under the stars of the prairies, and from those days he had cherished the illusion — certainly linked to nostalgia for the open spaces and the purity of that life — of being skilled in the kitchen. My mother, however, said that my father's pies were lead.

And this indeed was leaden fare that I valiantly strove to swallow.

Our eyes met. I saw that the mouthful my father had taken was not going down any more easily.

And how keenly then, through my own poor child's sorrow, did I gain a notion of my father's so much weightier sadness, the heaviness of life itself: that indigestible nutriment which this evening, as though it were forever, my father proffered me!

That night I was very sick with a serious attack of indigestion. My mother, having no inkling of what had taken place between the aged man and his Petite Misère, showered my father with reproaches. "To have her eat pie at ten o'clock at night! Have you lost your mind?"

With a sad smile and without pleading any excuse, he bowed his head; and, later, when he came to bring me a dose of medicine, his face was suffused with such grief that often I think it immortal.

Cornet at Night
Sinclair Ross

The wheat was ripe and it was Sunday. "Can't help it — I've got to cut," my father said at breakfast. "No use talking. There's a wind again and it's shelling fast."

"Not on the Lord's Day," my mother protested. "The horses stay in the stables where they belong. There's church this afternoon and I intend to ask Louise and her husband home for supper."

Ordinarily my father was a pleasant, accommodating little man, but this morning his wheat and the wind had lent him sudden steel. "No, today we cut," he met her evenly. "You and Tom go to church if you want to. Don't bother me."

"If you take the horses out today I'm through — I'll never speak to you again. And this time I mean it."

He nodded. "Good — if I'd known I'd have started cutting wheat on Sundays years ago."

"And that's no way to talk in front of your son. In the years to come he'll remember."

There was silence for a moment and then, as if in its clash with hers his will had suddenly found itself, my father turned to me.

"Tom, I need a man to stook for a few days and I want you to go to town tomorrow and get me one. The way the wheat's coming along so fast and the oats nearly ready too I can't afford the time. Take old Rock. You'll be safe with him."

But ahead of me my mother cried, "That's one thing I'll not stand for. You can cut your wheat or do anything else you like yourself, but you're not interfering with him. He's going to school tomorrow as usual."

My father bunched himself and glared at her. "No, for a change he's going to do what I say. The crop's more important than a day at school."

"But Monday's his music lesson day — and when will we have another teacher like Miss Wiggins who can teach him music too?"

"A dollar for lessons and the wheat shelling! When I was his age I didn't even get to school."

"Exactly," my mother scored, "and look at you today. Is it any wonder I want him to be different?"

He slammed out at that to harness his horses and cut his wheat, and away sailed my mother with me in her wake to spend an austere half-hour in the dark, hot plushy little parlour. It was a kind of vicarious atonement, I suppose, for we both took straight-backed leather chairs, and for all of the half-hour stared across the room at a big pansy-bordered motto on the opposite wall: *As for Me and My House We Will Serve the Lord.*

At last she rose and said, "Better run along and do your chores now, but hurry back. You've got to take your bath and change your clothes, and maybe help a little getting dinner for your father."

There was a wind this sunny August morning, tanged with freedom and departure, and from his stall my pony Clipper whinnied for a race with it. Sunday or not, I would ordinarily have had my gallop anyway, but today a sudden welling-up of social and religious conscience made me ask myself whether one in the family like my father wasn't bad enough. Returning to the house, I merely said that on such a fine day it seemed a pity to stay inside. My mother heard but didn't answer. Perhaps her conscience too was working. Perhaps after being worsted in the skirmish with my father, she was in no mood for granting dispensations. In any case I had to take my bath as usual, put on a clean white shirt, and change my overalls for knicker corduroys.

They squeaked, those corduroys. For three months now they had been spoiling all my Sundays. A sad, muted, swishing little squeak, but distinctly audible. Every step and there it was, as if I needed to be oiled. I had to wear them to church and Sunday-school; and after service, of course, while the grown-ups stood about gossiping, the other boys discovered my affliction. I sulked and fumed, but there was nothing to be done. Corduroys that had cost four-fifty simply couldn't be thrown away till they were well worn-out. My mother warned me that if I started sliding down the stable roof, she'd patch the seat and make me keep on wearing them.

With my customary little bow-legged sidle I slipped into the kitchen again to ask what there was to do. "Nothing but try to behave like a Christian and a gentleman," my mother answered stiffly. "Put on a tie, and shoes and stockings. Today your father is just about as much as I can bear."

"And then what?" I asked hopefully. I was thinking that I might take a drink to my father, but dared not as yet suggest it.

"Then you can stay quiet and read — and afterwards practise your music lesson. If your Aunt Louise should come she'll find that at least I bring my son up decently."

It was a long day. My mother prepared the midday meal as usual, but, to impress upon my father the enormity of his conduct, withdrew as soon as the food was served. When he was gone, she and I emerged to take our places at the table in an atmosphere of unappetizing righteousness. We didn't eat much. The food was cold, and my mother had no heart to warm it up. For relief at last she said, "Run along and feed the chickens while I change my dress. Since we aren't going to service today we'll read Scripture for a while instead."

And Scripture we did read, Isaiah, verse about, my mother in her black silk dress and rhinestone brooch, I in my corduroys and Sunday shoes that pinched. It was a very august afternoon, exactly like the tone that had persisted in my mother's voice since breakfast time. I think I might have openly rebelled, only for the hope that by compliance I yet might win permission for the trip to town with Rock. I was inordinately proud that my father had suggested it, and for his faith in me forgave him even Isaiah and the plushy afternoon. Whereas with my mother, I decided, it was a case of downright bigotry.

We went on reading Isaiah, and then for a while I played hymns on the piano. A great many hymns — even the ones with awkward sharps and accidentals that I'd never tried before — for, fearing visitors, my mother was resolved to let them see that she and I were uncontaminated by my father's sacrilege. But among these likely visitors was my Aunt Louise, a portly, condescending lady married to a well-off farmer with a handsome motor-car, and always when she came it was my mother's vanity to have me play for her a waltz or reverie, or "Holy Night" sometimes with variations. A man-child and prodigy might eclipse the motor-car. Presently she roused herself, and pretending mild reproof began, "Now, Tommy, you're going wooden on those hymns. For a change you'd better practise 'Sons of Liberty'. Your Aunt Louise will want to hear it, anyway."

There was a fine swing and vigour in this piece, but it was hard. Hard because it was so alive, so full of youth and head-high rhythm. It was a march, and it did march. I couldn't take time to practise at the hard spots slowly till I got them right, for I had to march too. I had to let my fingers sometimes miss a note or strike one wrong. Again and again this afternoon I started carefully, resolving to count right through, the way Miss Wiggins did, and as often I sprang ahead to lead my march a moment or two all dash and fired, and then fall stumbling in the bitter dust of dissonance. My mother didn't know. She thought that speed and perseverance would eventually get me there. She tapped her foot and smiled encouragement, and gradually as the afternoon wore on began to look a little disappointed that there were to be no visitors, after all. "Run along for the cows," she said at last, "while I get supper ready for your father. There'll be nobody here, so you can slip into your overalls again."

I looked at her a moment, and then asked: "What am I going to wear to town tomorrow? I might get grease or something on the corduroys."

For while it was always my way to exploit the future, I liked to do it rationally, within the limits of the sane and probable. On my way for the cows I wanted to live the trip to town tomorrow many times, with variations, but only on the explicit understanding that tomorrow there was to be a trip to town. I have always been tethered to reality, always compelled by an unfortunate kind of probity in my nature to prefer a bare-faced disappointment to the luxury of a future I have no just claims upon.

I went to town the next day, though not till there had been a full hour's argument that paradoxically enough gave all three of us the victory. For my Father had his way: I went; I had my way: I went; and in return for her consent my mother wrung a promise from him of a pair of new plush curtains for the parlour when the crop was threshed, and for me the metronome that Miss Wiggins declared was the only way I'd ever learn to keep in time on marching pieces like the "Sons of Liberty".

It was my first trip to town alone. That was why they gave me Rock, who was old and reliable and philosophic enough to meet motor-cars and the chance locomotive on an equal and even somewhat supercilious footing.

"Mind you pick somebody big and husky," said my father as he started for the field. "Go to Jenkins' store, and he'll tell you who's in town. Whoever it is, make sure he's stooked before."

"And mind it's somebody who looks like he washes himself," my mother warned, "I'm going to put clean sheets and pillowcases on the bunkhouse bed, but not for any dirty tramp or hobo."

By the time they had both finished with me there were a great many things to mind. Besides repairs for my father's binder, I was to take two crates of eggs each containing twelve dozen eggs to Mr. Jenkins' store and in exchange have a list of groceries filled. And to make it complicated, both quantity and quality of some of the groceries were to be determined by the price of eggs. Thirty cents a dozen, for instance, and I was to ask for coffee at sixty-five cents a pound. Twenty-nine cents a dozen and coffee at fifty cents a pound. Twenty-eight and no oranges. Thirty-one and bigger oranges. It was like decimals with Miss Wiggins, or two notes in the treble against three in the bass. For my father a tin of special blend tobacco, and my mother not to know. For my mother a box of face powder at the drugstore, and my father not to know. Twenty-five cents from my father on the side for ice-cream and licorice. Thirty-five from my mother for my dinner at the Chinese restaurant. And warning, of course, to take good care of Rock, speak politely to Mr. Jenkins, and see that I didn't get machine oil on my corduroys.

It was three hours to town with Rock, but I don't remember them. I remember nothing but a smug satisfaction with myself, an exhilarating conviction of importance and maturity — and that only by contrast with the sudden sag to embarrassed insignificance when finally old Rock and I drove up to Jenkins' store.

For a farm boy is like that. Alone with himself and his horse he cuts a fine figure. He is the measure of the universe. He foresees a great many encounters with life, and in them all acquits himself a little more than creditably. He is fearless, resourceful, a bit of a brag. His horse never contradicts.

But in town it is different. There are eyes here, critical, that pierce with a single glance the little bubble of his self-importance, and leave him dwindled smaller even than his normal size. It always happens that way. They are so superbly poised and sophisticated, these strangers, so completely masters of their situation as they loll in doorways and go sauntering up and down Main Street. Instantly he yields to them his place as measure of the universe, especially if he is a small boy wearing squeaky corduroys, especially if he has a worldly-wise old horse like Rock, one that knows his Main Streets, and will take them in nothing but his own slow philosophic stride.

We arrived all right. Mr. Jenkins was a little man with a freckled bald head, and when I carried in my two crates of eggs, one in each hand, and my legs bowed a bit, he said curtly, "Well, can't you set them down? My boy's delivering, and I can't take time to count them now myself."

"They don't need counting," I said politely. "Each layer holds two dozen, and each crate holds six layers. I was there. I saw my mother put them in."

At this a tall, slick-haired young man in yellow shoes who had been standing by the window turned around and said, "That's telling you, Jenkins — he was there." Nettled and glowering, Jenkins himself came round the counter and repeated, "So you were there, were you? Smart youngster! What did you say was your name?"

Nettled in turn to preciseness I answered, "I haven't yet. It's Thomas Dickson and my father's David Dickson, eight miles north of here. He wants a man to stook and was too busy to come himself."

He nodded, unimpressed, and then putting out his hand said, "Where's your list? Your mother gave you one, I hope?"

I said she had and he glowered again. "Then let's have it and come back in half an hour. Whether you were there or not, I'm going to count your eggs. How do I know that half of them aren't smashed?"

"That's right," agreed the young man, sauntering to the door and looking at Rock. "They've likely been bouncing along at a merry clip. You're quite sure, Buddy, that you didn't have a runaway?"

Ignoring the impertinence I staved off Jenkins. "The list, you see, has to be explained. I'd rather wait and tell you about it later on."

He teetered a moment on his heels and toes, then tried again. "I can read too. I make up orders every day. Just go away for a while — look for your man — anything."

"It wouldn't do," I persisted. "The way this one's written isn't what it really means. You'd need me to explain — "

He teetered rapidly. "Show me just one thing I don't know what it means."

"Oranges," I said, "but that's only oranges if eggs are twenty-nine cents or more — and bigger oranges if they're thirty-one. You see, you'd never understand — "

So I had my way and explained it all right then and there. What with eggs at twenty-nine and a half cents a dozen and my mother out a little in her calcualtions, it was somewhat confusing for a while; but after arguing a lot and pulling away the paper from each other that they were figuring on, the young man and Mr. Jenkins finally had it all worked out, with mustard and soap omitted altogether, and an extra half-dozen oranges thrown in. "Vitamins," the young man overruled me — "they make you grow" — and then with a nod towards an open biscuit box invited me to help myself.

I took a small one, and started up Rock again. It was nearly one o'clock now, so in anticipation of his noonday quart of oats he trotted off, a little more briskly, for the farmers' hitching-rail beside the lumber-yard. This was the quiet end of town. The air drowsed redolent of pine and tamarack, and resin simmering slowly in the sun. I poured out the oats and waited till he had finished. After the way the town had treated me it was comforting and peaceful to stand with my fingers in his mane, hearing him munch. It brought me a sense of place again in life. It made me feel almost as important as before. But when he finished and there was my own dinner to be thought about I found myself more of an alien in the town than ever, and felt the way to the little Chinese restaurant doubly hard. For Rock was older than I. Older and wiser, with a better understanding of important things. His philosophy included the relishing of oats even within a stone's throw of sophisticated Main Street. Mine was less mature.

I went, however, but I didn't have dinner. Perhaps it was my stomach, all puckered and tense with nervousness. Perhaps it was the restaurant itself, the pyramids of oranges in the window and the dark green rubber plant with the tropical-looking leaves, the indolent little Chinaman behind the counter and the dusky smell of last night's cigarettes that to my prairie nostrils was the orient itself, the exotic atmosphere about it all with which a meal of meat and vegetables and pie would have somehow simply jarred. I climbed onto a stool and ordered an ice-cream soda.

A few stools away there was a young man sitting. I kept watching him and wondering.

He was well-dressed, a nonchalance about his clothes that distinguished him from anyone I had ever seen, and yet at the same time it was a shabby suit with shiny elbows and threadbare cuffs. His hands were slender, almost a girl's hands, yet vaguely with their shapely quietness they troubled me, because, however slender and smooth, they were yet hands to be reckoned with, strong with a strength that was different from the rugged labour-strength I knew.

He smoked a cigarette, and blew rings towards the window. Different from the farmer boys I knew, yet different also from the young man with the yellow shoes in Jenkins' store. Staring out at it through the restaurant window he was as far away from Main Street as was I with plodding old Rock and my squeaky corduroys. I presumed for a minute or two an imaginary companionship. I finished my soda, and to be with him a little longer ordered lemonade. It was strangely important to be with him, to prolong a while this companionship. I hadn't the slightest hope of his noticing me, nor the slightest intention of obtruding myself. I just wanted to be there, to be assured by something I had never encountered before, to store it up for the three hours home with old Rock.

Then a big, unshaven man came in, and slouching onto the stool beside me said, "They tell me across the street you're looking for a couple of hands. What's your old man pay this year?"

"My father," I corrected him, "doesn't want a couple of men. He just wants one."

"I've got a pal," he insisted, "and we always go together."

I didn't like him. I couldn't help making contrasts with the cool, trim quietness of the young man sitting farther along. "What do you say?" he said as I sat silent, thrusting his stubby chin out almost over my lemonade. "We're ready any time."

"It's just one man my father wants," I said aloofly, drinking off my lemonade with a flourish to let him see I meant it. "And if you'll excuse me now — I've got to look for somebody else."

"What about this?" he intercepted me, and doubling up his arm displayed a hump of muscle that made me, if not more inclined to him, at least a little more deferential. "My pal's got plenty, too. We'll set up two stooks any day for anybody else's one."

"Not both," I edged away from him. "I'm sorry — you just wouldn't do."

He shook his head contemptuously. "Some farmer — just one man to stook."

"My father's a good farmer," I answered stoutly, rallying to the family honour less for its own sake than for what the young man on the other stool might think of us. "And he doesn't need just one man to stook. He's got three already. That's plenty other years, but this year the crop's so big he needs another. So there!"

"I can just see the place," he said, slouching to his feet and starting towards the door. "An acre or two of potatoes and a couple of dozen hens."

I glared after him a minute, then climbed back onto the stool and ordered another soda. The young man was watching me now in the big mirror behind the counter, and when I glanced up and met his eyes he gave a slow, half-smiling little nod of approval. And out of all proportion to anything it could mean, his nod encouraged me. I didn't flinch or fidget as I would have done had it been the young man with the yellow shoes watching me, and I didn't stammer over the confession that his amusement and appraisal somehow forced from me. "We haven't three men — just my father — but I'm to take one home today. The wheat's ripening fast this year and shelling, so he can't do it all himself."

He nodded again and then after a minute asked quietly, "What about me? Would I do?"

I turned on the stool and stared at him.

"I need a job, and if it's any recommendation there's only one of me."

"You don't understand," I started to explain, afraid to believe that perhaps he really did. "It's to stook. You have to be in the field by seven o'clock and there's only a bunkhouse to sleep in — a granary with a bed in it — "

"I know — that's about what I expect." He drummed his fingers a minute, then twisted his lips into a kind of half-hearted smile and went on, "They tell me a little toughening up is what I need. Outdoors, and plenty of good hard work — so I'll be like the fellow that just went out."

The wrong hands: white slender fingers, I knew they'd never do — but catching the twisted smile again I pushed away my soda and said quickly, "Then we'd better start right away. It's three hours home, and I've still some places to go. But you can get in the buggy now, and we'll drive around together."

We did. I wanted it that way, the two of us there, to settle scores with Main Street. I wanted to capture some of old Rock's disdain and unconcern; I wanted to know what it felt like to take young men with yellow shoes in my stride, to be preoccupied, to forget them the moment that we separated. And I did. "My name's Philip," the stranger said as we drove from Jenkins' to the drugstore. "Philip Coleman — usually just Phil," and companionably I responded, "Mine's Tommy Dickson. For the last year, though, my father says I'm getting big and should be called just Tom."

That was what mattered now, the two of us there, and not the town at all. "Do you drive yourself all the time?" he asked, and nonchalant and off-hand I answered, "You don't really have to drive old Rock. He just goes, anyway. Wait till you see my chestnut three-year-old. Clipper I call him. Tonight after supper if you like you can take him for a ride."

But since he'd never learned to ride at all he thought Rock would do better for a start, and then we drove back to the restaurant for his cornet and valise.

"Is it something to play?" I asked as we cleared the town. "Something like a bugle?"

He picked up the black leather case from the floor of the buggy and held it on his knee. "Something like that. Once I played a bugle too. A cornet's better, though."

"And you mean you can play the cornet?"

He nodded. "I play in a band. At least I did play in a band. Perhaps if I get along all right with the stooking I will again some time."

It was later that I pondered this, how stooking for my father could have anything to do with going back to play in a band.

At the moment I confided, "I've never heard a cornet — never even seen one. I suppose you still play it sometimes — I mean at night, when you've finished stooking."

Instead of answering directly he said, "That means you've never heard a band either." There was surprise in his voice, almost incredulity, but it was kindly. Somehow I didn't feel ashamed because I had lived all my eleven years on a prairie farm, and knew nothing more than Miss Wiggins and my Aunt Louise's gramophone. He went on, "I was younger than you are now when I started playing in a band. Then I was with an orchestra a while — then with the band again. It's all I've done ever since."

It made me feel lonely for a while, isolated from the things in life that mattered, but, brightening presently, I asked, "Do you know a piece called "Sons of Liberty"? Four flats in four-four time?"

He thought hard a minute, and then shook his head. "I'm afraid I don't — not by name anyway. Could you whistle a bit of it?"

I whistled two pages, but still he shook his head. "A nice tune, though," he conceded. "Where did you learn it?"

"I haven't yet," I explained. "Not properly, I mean. It's been my lesson for the last two weeks, but I can't keep up to it."

He seemed interested, so I went on and told him about my lessons and Miss Wiggins, and how later on they were going to buy me a metronome so that when I played a piece I wouldn't always be running away with it, "Especially a march. It keeps pulling you along the way it really ought to go until you're all mixed up and have to start at the beginning again. I know I'd do better if I didn't feel that way, and could keep slow and steady like Miss Wiggins."

But he said quickly, "No, that's the right way to feel — you've just got to learn to harness it. It's like old Rock here and Clipper. The way you are, you're Clipper. But if you weren't that way, if you didn't get excited and wanted to run

sometimes, you'd just be Rock: You see? Rock's easier to
handle than Clipper, but at his best he's a sleepy old plow-
horse. Clipper's harder to handle — he may even cost you some
tumbles. But finally get him broken in and you've got a horse
that amounts to something. You wouldn't trade him for a
dozen like Rock."

It was a good enough illustration, but it slandered Rock.
And he was listening. I know — because even though like me
he had never heard a cornet before, he had experience enough
to accept it at least with tact and manners.

For we hadn't gone much farther when Philip, noticing the
way I kept watching the case that was still on his knee, undid
the clasps and took the cornet out. It was a very lovely cornet,
shapely and eloquent, gleaming in the August sun like pure and
mellow gold. I couldn't restrain myself. I said, "Play it — play
it now — just a little bit to let me hear." And in response,
smiling at my earnestness, he raised it to his lips.

But there was only one note — only one fragment of a note
— and then away went Rock. I'd never have believed he had
it in him. With a snort and plunge he was off the road and into
the ditch — then out of the ditch again and off at a breakneck
gallop across the prairie. There were stones and badger holes,
and he spared us none of them. The egg-crates full of groceries
bounced out, then the tobacco, then my mother's face powder.
"Whoa Rock!" I cried, "Whoa, Rock!" but in the rattle and
whir of wheels I don't suppose he even heard. Philip couldn't
help much because he had his cornet to hang on to. I tried to
tug on the reins, but at such a rate across the prairie it took me
all my time to keep from following the groceries. He was a big
horse, Rock, and once under way had to run himself out. Or
he may have thought that if he gave us a thorough shaking-up
we would be too subdued when it was over to feel like taking
him seriously to task. Anyway, that was how it worked out. All
I dared to do was run round to pat his sweaty neck and say,
"Good Rock, good Rock — nobody's going to hurt you."

Besides there were the groceries to think about, and my

mother's box of face powder. And his pride and reputation at stake, Rock had made it a runaway worthy of the horse he really was. We found the powder smashed open and one of the egg-crates cracked. Several of the oranges had rolled down a badger hole, and couldn't be recovered. We spent nearly ten minutes sifting raisins through our fingers, and still they felt a little gritty. "There were extra oranges," I tried to encourage Philip, "and I've seen my mother wash her raisins." He looked at me dubiously, and for a few minutes longer worked away trying to mend the egg-crate.

We were silent for the rest of the way home. We thought a great deal about each other, but asked no questions. Even though it was safely away in its case again I could still feel the cornet's presence as if it were a living thing. Somehow its gold and shapeliness persisted, transfiguring the day, quickening the dusty harvest fields to a gleam and lustre like its own. And I felt assured, involved. Suddenly there was a force in life, a current, an inevitability, carrying me along too. The questions they would ask when I reached home — the difficulties in making them understand that faithful old Rock had really run away — none of it now seemed to matter. This stranger with the white, thin hands, this gleaming cornet that as yet I hadn't even heard, intimately and enduringly now they were my possessions.

When we reached home my mother was civil and no more. "Put your things in the bunkhouse," she said, "and then wash here. Supper'll be ready in about an hour."

It was an uncomfortable meal. My father and my mother kept looking at Philip and exchanging glances. I told them about the cornet and the runaway, and they listened stonily. "We've never had a harvest-hand before that was a musician too," my mother said in a somewhat thin voice. "I suppose, though, you do know how to stook?"

I was watching Philip desperately and for my sake he lied, "Yes, I stooked last year. I may have a blister or two by this time tomorrow, but my hands will toughen up."

"You don't as a rule do farm work?" my father asked.

And Philip said, "No, not as a rule."

There was an awkward silence, so I tried to champion him. "He plays his cornet in a band. Ever since he was my age — that's what he does."

Glances were exchanged again. The silence continued.

I had been half-intending to suggest that Philip bring his cornet into the house to play it for us, I perhaps playing with him on the piano, but the parlour with its genteel plushiness was a room from which all were excluded but the equally genteel — visitors like Miss Wiggins and the minister — and gradually as the meal progressed I came to understand that Philip and his cornet, so far as my mother was concerned, had failed to qualify.

So I said nothing when he finished his supper, and let him go back to the bunkhouse alone. "Didn't I say to have Jenkins pick him out?" my father stormed as soon as he had gone. "Didn't I say somebody big and strong?"

"He's tall," I countered, "and there wasn't anybody else except two men, and it was the only way they'd come."

"You mean you didn't want anybody else. A cornet player! Fine stooks he'll set up." And then, turning to my mother, "It's your fault — you and your nonsense about music lessons. If you'd listen to me sometimes, and try to make a man of him."

"I do listen to you," she answered quickly. "It's because I've had to listen to you now for thirteen years that I'm trying to make a different man of him. If you'd go to town yourself instead of keeping him out of school — and do your work in six days a week like decent people. I told you yesterday that in the long run it would cost you dear."

I slipped away and left them. The chores at the stable took me nearly an hour; and then , instead of returning to the house, I went over to see Philip. It was dark now, and there was a smoky lantern lit. He sat on the only chair, and in a hospitable silence motioned me to the bed. At once he ignored and accepted me. It was as if we had always known each other and long outgrown the need of conversation. He smoked, and blew rings towards the open door where the warm fall night encroached. I waited, eager, afraid lest they call me to the house, yet knowing that I must wait. Gradually the flame in the lantern smoked the glass till scarcely his face was left visible. I sat tense, expectant, wondering who he was, where he came from, why he should be here to do my father's stooking.

There were no answers, but presently he reached for his cornet. In the dim, soft darkness I could see it glow and quicken. And I remember still what a long and fearful moment it was, crouched and steeling myself, waiting for him to begin.

And I was right: when they came the notes were piercing, golden as the cornet itself, and they gave life expanse that it had never known before. They floated up against the night, and each for a moment hung there clear and visible. Sometimes they mounted poignant and sheer. Sometimes they soared and then, like a bird alighting, fell and brushed earth again.

It was "To the Evening Star". He finished it and told me. He told me the names of all the other pieces that he played: an "Ave Maria", "Song of India", a serenade — all bright through the dark like slow, suspended lightning, chilled sometimes with a glimpse of the unknown. Only for Philip there I could not have endured it. With my senses I clung hard to him — the acrid smell of his cigarettes, the titled profile daubed with smoky light.

Then abruptly he stood up, as if understanding, and said, "Now we'd better have a march, Tom — to bring us back where we belong. A cornet can be good fun, too, you know. Listen to this one and tell me."

He stood erect, head thrown back exactly like a picture in my reader of bugler boy, and the notes came flashing gallant through the night until the two of us went swinging along in step with them a hundred thousand strong. For this was another march that did march. It marched us miles. It made the feet eager and the heart brave. It said that life was worth the living and bright as morning shone ahead to show the way.

When he had finished and put the cornet away I said, "There's a field right behind the house that my father started cutting this afternoon. If you like we'll go over now for a few minutes and I'll show you how to stook. . . . You see, if you set your sheaves on top of the stubble they'll be over again in half an hour. That's how everybody does at first but it's wrong. You've got to push the butts down hard, right to the ground — like this, so they bind with the stubble. At a good slant, see, but not too much. So they'll stand the wind and still shed water if it rains."

It was too dark for him to see much, but he listened hard and finally succeeded in putting up a stook or two that to my touch seemed firm enough. Then my mother called, and I had to slip away fast so that she would think I was coming from the bunkhouse. "I hope he stooks as well as he plays," she said when I went in. "Just the same, you should have done as your father told you, and picked a likelier man to see us through the fall."

My father came in from the stable then, and he, too, had been listening. With a wondering, half-incredulous little movement of his head he made acknowledgement.

"Didn't I tell you he could?" I burst out, encouraged to indulge my pride in Philip. "Didn't I tell you he could play?"

But with sudden anger in his voice he answered, "And what if he can! It's a man to stook I want. Just look at the hands on him. I don't think he's ever seen a farm before."

It was helplessness, though, not anger. Helplessness to escape his wheat when wheat was not enough, when something more than wheat had just revealed itself. Long after they were both asleep I remembered, and with a sharp foreboding that we might have to find another man, tried desperately to sleep myself. Because if I'm up in good time, I rallied all my faith in life, "I'll be able to go to the field with him and at least make sure he's started right. And he'll maybe do. I'll ride down after school and help till supper time. My father's reasonable."

Only in such circumstances, of course, and after such a day,

I couldn't sleep till nearly morning, with the result that when at last my mother wakened me there was barely time to dress and ride to school. But of the day I spent there I remember nothing. Nothing except the midriff clutch of dread that made it a long day — nothing, till straddling Clipper at four again, I galloped him straight to the far end of the farm where Philip that morning had started to work.

Only Philip, of course, wasn't there. I think it was what all day I had been expecting. I pulled Clipper up short and sat staring at the stooks. Three or four acres of them — crooked and dejected as if he had never heard about pushing the butts down hard into the stubble. I sat and stared till Clipper himself swung round and started for home. He wanted to run, but because there was nothing left now but the half-mile ahead of us, I held him to a walk. Just to prolong a little the possibility that I had misunderstood things. To wonder within the limits of the sane and probable if tonight he would play his cornet again.

When I reached the house my father was already there, eating an early supper. "I'm taking him back to town," he said quietly. "He tried hard enough — he's just not used to it. The sun was hot today; he lasted till about noon. We're starting in a few minutes, so you'd better go out and see him."

He looked older now, stretched out limp on the bed, his face haggard. I tiptoed close to him anxiously, afraid to speak. He pulled his mouth sidewise in a smile at my concern, then motioned me to sit down. "Sorry I didn't do better," he said. "I'll have to come back another year and have another lesson."

I clenched my hands and clung hard to the promise that I knew he couldn't keep. I wanted to rebel against what was happening, against the clumsiness and crudity of life, but instead I stood quiet a moment, almost passive, then wheeled away and carried out his cornet to the buggy. My mother was already there, with a box of lunch and some ointment for his sunburn. She said she was sorry things had turned out this way, and thanking her politely he said that he was sorry too. My father looked uncomfortable, feeling, no doubt, that we were all unjustly blaming everything on him. It's like that on a farm. You always have to put the harvest first.

And that's all there is to tell. He waved going through the gate; I never saw him again. We watched the buggy down the road to the first turn, then with quick resentment in her voice my mother said,"Didn't I say that the little he gained would in the long run cost him dear? Next time he'll maybe listen to me — and remember the Sabbath Day."

What exactly she was thinking I never knew. Perhaps of the crop and the whole day's stooking lost. Perhaps of the stranger who had come with his cornet for a day, and then as meaninglessly gone again. For she had been listening, too, and she may have understood. A harvest, however lean, is certain every year; but a cornet at night is golden only once.

Anemone
Dorothy M. Powell

Our first summer without Dad I thought we would have gone anywhere but Sandspit Inn. Yet here was Mother driving the same tree-columned road without seeming to recall how Dad used to slow the car at every curve. A glimpse of the Straits through an arch of stone. A froth of green water beneath an old bridge.

"I hope you packed some old jeans," she was saying. "Last year, with that beach crowd of yours, you ruined every pair of slacks."

I didn't bother to remind her that it was only the end of June. My "beach crowd", as she put it, usually arrived a month later. This early in the season, the Inn would be almost deserted.

Instead, I observed cooly, "You're driving too fast."

She shot me an arch little look and laughed. "You're just miffed because you want the wheel."

Lately, that's the way we've been. Ever since Dad had the heart attack and left us so suddenly. Mother keeps putting on this forced togetherness act. Myself, never seeming able to say what I mean.

Slowing the car, she pulled over to the shoulder. "C'mon honey. Stop sulking. You can drive if you want."

I looked at her pretty, unlined face and hated her for not knowing how I felt. "Forget it," I told her, rudely. "We're almost there, anyway."

Brows peaked, she turned again onto the highway. "Not exactly a ray of sunshine, are you?"

My throat tightened. On the roadbank, clumps of Indian paintbrush burned scarlet and all I could see was Dad with his camera in that exact spot last year. How *could* she forget!

Nothing seemed changed, though, about the Inn. Its clapboard still shone white against dark pine. Its windows, facing the straits, still watched waves marching in blue lines to break ranks on the rocky shore. The sloping lawns were brilliant with flowerbeds and the long, yellow sandspit fingered the inlet beckoning me to follow. Other summers, when the tide was out, I loved to walk to the finger's tip. Standing there, I used to get this weird feeling that I'd left myself back on the shore. No longer Rissa Munroe, I became something wild and free, a creature who could maybe walk the water to where it met the sky. Now, driving up to the Inn's front entrance, I couldn't think of a better place to be — at the very tip of that spit.

The owners, Mr. and Mrs. Gagliano, came hurrying to greet us while, on the lawn, their son Tony stood leaning on a rake. Still doing odd jobs, I thought, and looking much taller than last time. By now, he must have finished university.

Always shy, he surprised me by lifting an arm in welcome and coming to help with the bags.

Following Tony up the polished staircase, I waited while he deposited my cases at the foot of the bed. "Where do these go? In your mother's room?"

I nodded, remembering with a pang that the room was once shared by Dad. I could see Tony remembering, too. "Rissa," he began. "I'm sorry. . . ."

Turning abruptly to the window overlooking the Inn's kitchen garden, I said, "Thanks," shaken by the warmth of his dark eyes. I had never grown to know Tony. Possibly because he rarely mingled with guests, preferring to spend most of his time on the loneliest part of the shore.

My back still to the room, I didn't realize he had left till I heard him telling Mother that we were the first to arrive. "Tonight, there'll be two other families," he said.

"Good," came the bright reply. "At least, we'll have a foursome for bridge."

I snapped open my vanity and ripped a fingernail. She couldn't wait, could she? To start having fun!

Unpacked, I wandered downstairs to the dining room where Tony's mother was setting our favorite table in the bow window. Last year, Dad had joked about it. "You shouldn't put us here," he had laughed. "It's always a toss-up as to which is best. Your cooking or the view."

"If Mother wants to know where I am," I told Mrs. Gagliano, "I'll be down on the beach."

The sandspit, hardpacked and ribboned with water, proved easy walking. Spiced with the ancient smell of the sea, waves raced past giving my escape a dreamlike speed. That other Rissa, with her hurt and her tears, I left far behind on the shore. *"Come back!"* she called. But I didn't want to hear, and closed my ears to everything but the restless rush of water.

"Ree-sah!" The voice, louder and deeper, held definite command. "Get back! The tide's coming in!"

I turned, then, to see Tony running toward me. Leaping a sudden network of small rivers, he sloshed up to his ankles where the sea had claimed the spit. Halfway back to shore, the spit had already disappeared beneath a foam of water and I came to an abrupt halt. But Tony plunged in, his angry face telling me louder than words what to do.

On shore, he gave me a disgusted look. "Idiot! You *know* about that tide!"

"I'm a strong swimmer," I informed him, stiffly. "Or have you forgotten?"

I knew that he hadn't. Last summer, when four of us tried to best this tide, Tony had made it icily clear what he thought. We took precautions, of course. A boat and each swimmer with a lifeline. Tony, we said, was a drag; too quiet and forever sitting on some remote pile of rocks.

"Thanks," I mumbled. "For coming to the rescue." Usually, Rissa Munroe, summertime fun-girl, felt no reason to explain her actions to anyone. So the next words didn't come very easily. "I wasn't thinking about tides. You wouldn't understand."

"Try me," he offered.

A sudden breeze whipped my wet hair, spattering drops, and I shivered.

"Tonight?" he persisted.

"Tomorrow," I said, not sure I wanted to talk with anyone about anything.

The evening seemed endless. At dinner, Mother sat in the chair which used to be Dad's. Eating with evident enjoyment, she made me feel slightly sick. In crisp, green cotton, a bulky sweater over slim shoulders, her hair glinted red in the sun. Sometimes we are mistaken for sisters and I used to think it fun. Now, I resented the resemblance: she had no heart, no tears, no memory.

I pushed back my chair and she looked up, fork poised above her plate. "Not hungry?"

I shook my head, steering blindly for the front door and nearly colliding with Tony.

Outside, the air was chilly, the ocean gray. Except for a

mustard-coloured sun making a feeble attempt at a sunset, the whole scene looked bleak. Black rocks. Black pines. Black for the end of Dad. Clinging to the veranda rail, I shook it with my sobs until Tony's hand closed on my shoulder. "Rissa," he pleaded. "Don't."

"She sent you," I accused.

He nodded. "She's worried about you."

I swung on him. "Worried I won't play the game."

To his raised brows, I gave the bitter answer. "The name of the game is be gay and forget!" I pointed a shaky finger at the window. "That's not a game, any more. That's for real!"

Tony's eyes followed my finger to where Mother chatted happily with the newly arrived guests. "You're wrong, you know," he said. "About your mother."

I jerked away. "How would *you* know?" I cried. "I didn't say that I did," he admitted, quietly. "Look. Let's meet in the morning — down by the rocks where we can talk."

"What's it to be?" I asked, brightly. "A lesson in psychology? Or natural science?" Well aware that Tony was a frustrated naturalist, I knew that Mr. Gagliano expected his son to carry on with the family hotel.

Not answering, Tony simply smiled and left me alone.

That night I went to bed early, and awakened to the Straits sparkling with sun and waves all crackled with white. Last summer and every summer before, Mother and Dad used to walk their after-breakfast mile along the beach and I wondered aloud about her plans for the morning.

"Golfing," she told me across the table. "Then lunch at the clubhouse with the Setons, the people who just arrived. You went to bed before I could introduce you." It was Mother's subtle was of asking, "Why?"

"Well," I said, "have fun." She didn't miss the sarcasm. Immediately sorry for the resulting flinch, I was about to say so when her face lifted in welcome. "Good morning. Come and meet my daughter."

I stayed only long enough for introductions. Then excused myself.

From the steps at the lawn's edge, I could see Tony perched on his favourite rock and outlined against the sea. This stretch of shore we had christened the Giant's Playpen, the clutter of squared-off rocks resembling outsize blocks which some monster-baby might have thrown here.

Hearing my sneakers on tiled stone, his smile gleamed white in the sun. Still an hour before tide-time, I knew that Tony's rock would be the only one remaining above water-level. For a while we'd be marooned there and the idea was not unpleasant. Together, we could sit untouched while the ocean hissed at our feet.

He held out a sea-damp hand. "Glad you made it before the tide. There's something I want you to see."

I remembered, then, that I was slated for analysis and wondered at my eagerness to be bored. "I can always race the tide to shore," I told him airily.

Without comment, he shifted a little to make room on the narrow shelf. "Make yourself comfortable."

"How'd you know I'd fit?"

He grinned. "I only ask girls size ten."

Indicating a small rock basin about three feet lower than our perch, he changed the subject. "Look at this pool. What do you see?"

I shrugged. The pool resembled any number of amber-coloured puddles left there by the tide. "Water," I said.

He clucked his tongue. "Ree-sah." And my name rounded like the sea-sigh at the end of the spit. "Let yourself go," he commanded. "Sink."

At first, it was a bit like self-hypnosis. My own face wavered up at me, eyes the colour of sky and hair as undulating brown. Then, gradually, I sank beneath myself and the surface.

With a feeling of utter peace, I felt as if, somehow, I had penetrated the serene centre of one glistening drop of dew.

Tony was there. I was there. Yet we seemed suspended, hardly breathing, in another world.

The sea whispered, climbing against our rock, the slight vibration quivering seaweed in our tiny pool forest. Then, with each succeeding wave, the forest, the little clearing began to come to life. Transparent submarines started rocketing about. "Shrimp," Tony said.

At my startled gasp, he added, *"Nudibranch,"* when a lacy branch began walking upside down on our watery sky. I shook my head. I wanted only to look. The lesson could come later.

I didn't have long to wait. The sea, no longer gentle, foamed and eddied against the lower rocks, surging up the sides of our perch, then receding.

And the pool, no longer heaven, became a small hell. The seaweed forest bent, smothered beneath the first wave. The lovely mini-mountain scenery became a sudden series of open shells. Mouths to devour the unwary. From cracks and crannies appeared gills and tentacles, waving about in a frenzy of foam. All with one awful purpose. To fill a stomach!

I wrenched my hand from Tony's — all this time it had been linked with his — and leaped to my feet. "This!" I shouted above the water's din. *"This* is what you want me to see. Another way to die!"

I would have left him, then. But there was nowhere to go. Our rock was surrounded by sea. I stood trapped, hugging myself and shivering. Till Tony, easing to his feet, put an arm about my shoulders.

"Another way to live, Rissa," he corrected. "Something always dies so something else may live." Last year, I would have thought it a really square thing to say. Now, without words, I turned it over in my mind.

"My father, too?" I asked, coldly.

His face went blank and I got bitter pleasure out of knowing he had no answer. "My father dies so that Mother and I can live," I persisted. "Is *that* it?"

"It has to work that way," he admitted, finally. "Everything else does."

I shuddered and his arm tightened, pulling me down to the rock. I don't know how long we sat there, huddled silently together while the tide slowly withdrew. It left rocks shining in the sun and seaweed streaming peacock blues.

The pool, once again crystal clear, lay quiet at our feet. Above its rim, a huge mauve anemone flowered in brief beauty. "Look," I said. "A flower for the dead."

"It's dying, too," he told me, bluntly. "Grown too big for its home. The tide barely reached it. No tide, no food."

Whether it was the tide's cleansing effect or that Tony seemed as hopeless as myself, I wanted for some reason to cheer him. "Sea anemones can move, can't they?"

He nodded. "On their spines. This one got too lazy. Just anchored there and waited for the sea to serve it dinner."

"You mean it didn't adapt to change."

His face brightened. "That's right."

I knew, then, what Tony in his strange, sweet way had been trying to tell me. I couldn't go on living the same as when Dad was here. Neither could my mother. She, at least, was trying to adapt to a new life without him.

"Maybe," I said, slowly, "we could save that anemone."

And for the next two weeks, we tried. We spent every moment of Tony's time off on the largest rock in the Giant's Playpen. We watered the anemone with sea water when the tide was too low. We caught miniscule shrimp and crab to feed its waving petals. We even tried to pry it loose. Our hair became so spiked with spray, our jeans and sneakers so continually damp, we began to look like sea creatures ourselves. Usually it took an hour just to scrape myself clean before golfing with Mother.

The day the anemone died was the day we left the Inn. Early in the morning, Tony and I found it shrivelled brown and we regarded it sadly. "Guess I could use some of my own good advice," he said, finally.

"How do you mean?"

"Get up enough courage to tell Dad I intend to be a natural scientist. That I won't be carrying on at the Inn."

I looked up, dismayed. "That means you'll be taking the post-grad course in California?"

His eyes crinkled. "You don't approve?"

"You'll be too far away," I told him honestly.

"I'll be back every summer," he promised.

Elegy for My Family
Kathy Roberts

We sang four part
Harmony,
We performed
Well
In public
But two
Couldn't agree
At rehersal
So,
One member was
Cut
By the other.

I sing in two trios,
Usually with the
Alto and tenor,
Other times with the
Tenor and bass.

I think maybe
When my voice
Develops more,
I'll sing

Solo,
Or have
My own group,
A duet.

The Pinch Hitters
D. P. Barnhouse

He can't fool me, Mark thought resentfully, with that business about dry rot. The old cottonwood had been there ever since he could remember. His own father had supervised the building of the tree house from his wheelchair on the lawn. That was only three years ago. If the tree was dying as William said, wouldn't his father have known it, for pity's sake!

Mark glared at his stepfather's broad back as he followed him into the kitchen. His mother took a platter of chicken from the warming oven. William gave her a little hug.

"Are you feeling all right?" he asked a bit anxiously. "Joe Miller's got a badly foundered mare and I promised I'd take a look at her after supper. I may be late."

"I'm fine, William," his mother said. "Besides, I have Mark here if anything goes wrong. Just you get busy on that chicken before it's cold and don't worry your head. My goodness, you take this baby as seriously as a five-year drought."

"It is," William said. "To me."

She went to fetch the cream from the porch cooler. "Remember, Mark," William said. "You've got till Saturday, then down comes the whole shebang. I should have done it long ago but I figured you'd want to salvage your tree house first. . . . Saturday, mind."

Mark maintained a stony silence through dinner. You couldn't tell him anything about stepfathers. Hadn't he read *David Copperfield*? They were all the same. They gave you this "let's be pals" stuff and got your own mother on their side and then they began to take over. William was fine before his father died. Mark was glad to see him come around because there was so much work and his mother looked so tired and discouraged trying to keep up with it. William owned the half section next to theirs but having him for a neighbour was quite different from having him for a stepfather. Not that he didn't have fun with William sometimes; like the day they caught the big bull trout above the beaver dam — and of course, the day he brought Sabrina.

That was the best thing Mark could say for his stepfather. He'd given him Sabrina who was soft as dandelion fluff and good to have purring beside you at night when you felt lonely and sort of left out of things.

Now, since Sabrina's kittens had come, she hadn't time to visit him at night or to hone her needle-sharp claws on his trouser legs at the breakfast table.

He supposed it would be the same with his mother when she had the baby. She and William tried to include him in their discussions about it but Mark always found reasons to be excused. Either the pony needed a rub down or the hens needed water. Actually, he was glad to escape their beaming faces and take refuge in his tree house. High up in the green jungle of the cottonwood's leaves he tried desparately to remember that last happy summer before his father's last illness. After three years, images get pretty blurred — even the sound of a voice.

Now, helping his mother clear away the supper things, he tried again but the face wouldn't come clear. In his green cave in the cottonwood, the rustling of the leaves was like a thousand voices talking to him. It was easier there to remember.

He heard the pickup in the driveway. William left the motor running and put his head in the back door to caution Mark. "You keep an eye on your mother, mind."

Mark didn't answer. It annoyed him, the habit William had of tacking "mind" onto everything he said. It was neither a question nor a statement, but something halfway between.

Well, if "mind" meant obey, William had another think coming when it came to the tree house. He'd see what his mother had to say about that! Surely she'd be on his side this once.

She bent to take a pan of raisin cookies from the oven. Her face was flushed and she had a hard time straightening up.

"It's too hot to bake in this weather," she said. "I should have had more sense."

"Mom, William says I've got to move my tree house."

"Mark, don't you think you might manage to call William 'Father' once in a while. I think it would please him."

"But he's *not* my father."

She wiped her apron over her damp face and looked at him for a long moment without speaking.

"Didn't you do some pinch hitting in the league finals last year?"

"Sure. Don't you remember the homer I racked up for Chuck Wilson?"

"Well . . . it seems to me that you and William are both pinch hitters, sort of, so you might as well play ball. Isn't that right?"

Mark was in no mood for sermons. He was too full of his grievance. "The reason I gotta move it," he blurted out, "is because he's got some crazy idea about cutting down the cottonwood because it's dangerous."

"That's a pity," his mother said. "It's shaded the porch for so many years."

"Mom, do I *have* to?"

"I'm sure William wouldn't sacrifice that tree without good reason. You'd best do what he says."

"But gee whillikers, I don't see . . ."

"No back chat. You get busy and do what William says, mind." Even his mother had caught that silly habit. Well, he *did* mind and he'd do what William said when he was good and ready. A sudden gust came in through the open door, stirring up the sultry air.

"I think it's working up to a storm," his mother said. "No wonder, after all this heat. I think I'll lie down for a while. I'm a bit done in."

Mark sat in the open doorway of the feed shed and watched the sky blacken to the south. Lightning stabbed through the gathering thunderheads. A cooling rain would be nice after the long dry spell. He hoped it wouldn't pass over like it did last week, soaking the crops to the south but leaving their own fields still parched.

Sabrina stalked by him on velvet paws into the dusty gloom of the shed. Mousing again — to stuff those kittens. She took up her position on a pile of grain sacks and pretended she was stone. He made low coaxing sounds. She glared at him as if to say, "Don't bother me when I have serious things to attend to." Later, she changed her vantage point to the window ledge. He marvelled at how she could thread her way through the maze of 'oil cans, binder twine and assorted bottles of veterinary remedies without disturbing as much as a cob-web.

He was so absorbed in watching her that he jumped when the door slammed shut. There was an enormous clap of thunder and the wind shook the shed as Sabrina might shake a rat. When the rain came you could scarcely hear its drumming on the roof for the increasing violence of the wind. How suddenly it had risen. He opened the door and Sabrina streaked for the house. He was enjoying the strange darkness and the tumult of sound when above the wind he heard his mother calling him.

He was drenched before he was halfway across the yard. The wind clawed at him so that he had to cling to the porch railing. His mother was at the phone, just inside the front vestibule. Her eyes looked enormous.

"I can't get your father," she said. "Maybe you'd better saddle up Ginger, just in case. I think the baby's coming."

The pony was terrified of lightning. He had trouble getting the bit in her mouth and persuading her to leave the stable. Now the excitement of the storm was changed into menace. He tied the bridle rope to the cottonwood and ran into the house.

"Hello," his mother was repeating desperately. "Please get off the line. I've got to get through to Joe Miller or to Doctor Jensen. Hello — hello."

Mark tried to close the door behind him but the force of the wind tore it from his hands. Almost at the same moment the house reeled under a crashing blow. His mother lay in a crumpled heap under the dangling telephone receiver. There was a steady grinding noise on the roof. Shattered branches thrust into the vestibule through the open door. Then he knew it was the tree that had fallen, just as William said it might.

"Well," his mother said dazedly, opening her eyes. "And I always said I wasn't the fainting type. What hit us?"

"The cottonwood," Mark said. "It's fallen on the porch roof."

"You'd better help me to the couch. Then keep calling till you get someone — anyone." Her teeth were chattering, whether from chills or fright he couldn't tell. He made her comfortable and covered her with a blanket. He was afraid for the pony left tied to the tree. He looked out the living room window but could see nothing but a mass of foliage and the phone line dangling. He hated to alarm his mother but he had to tell her.

"I can't phone, Mom, the tree's taken the lines down. But don't you worry. Ginger and I can make it to Miller's in twenty minutes. We can phone the doctor from there. Will you be all right alone for a little while?"

"Yes," she said through tight lips. "But *do* hurry."

The front doorway was blocked by shattered branches. He left by the back door, praying that the pony would be all right. There was a frayed end of rope hanging from the fallen trunk. She must have broken away. He whistled for her but the wind tore the sound to shreds and drowned the pieces in its greater sound. It's useless to search, he thought. If she bolted, she could be miles away by now. He couldn't alarm his mother further. There was only one thing to do — get to Miller's on foot, as fast as he could.

By the time he reached the main road, he was out of breath

and buffetted about like a cork in a mill race. If only the wind were with him instead of against him. He leaned into it, cupping his hands over his mouth to save what breath he had. He seemed to be advancing at a snail's pace. It would take him hours at this rate. The road was littered with debris from the storm. The wind flung a branch under his feet and he tripped and fell. When he got up, his ankle turned under him. He went white with the pain. He tried to walk on it but it was useless. He thought of his mother lying alone at home and panic filled him.

He was stripping twigs from the fallen branch to fashion himself a cane when he saw headlights stab through the gloom up ahead. He prayed they wouldn't turn off the main road before they reached him. He stood up and waved his arms madly. As the vehicle came closer, he saw it was their pickup. William nearly ran him down before slamming on his brakes. Mark tumbled in beside him.

"Boy, am I glad to see you," he said. "We've got to get Doc Jensen. The baby's coming."

"Something told me to get on home," William said.

The storm had raged itself out and a pink glow warmed the east. Mark and William sat on the bole of the fallen cottonwood and watched the lights still burning in the upstairs bedroom.

"It's taking a long time," William said. "By the way, how's the lame pastern — hurt much?"

Mark looked down at his neatly bound ankle. "Hardly at all," he said. "You sure tie a good bandage, William."

"Just finished practising on Joe Miller's mare and she's a lot more ornery than you are." William grinned and scratched the ears of Sabrina the fickle, who was contentedly honing her claws on his thighs. Her quiet purring filled the small silence that followed.

"I'm sorry about the tree," Mark said. "Will it cost a lot to fix the roof?"

"Can't rightly say till we haul her off. Probably a little

lumber and a lot of work is what it'll amount to."

"Couldn't we salvage some lumber from the tree house?"

"We could," William said, "but I figured you'd want to rebuild it — maybe in that old lodge pine out by the back corral."

"I reckon I've outgrown that house," Mark said.

There was enough room left for Doc to stick his head out through the front door. "You can come and see your son now," he hollered at William. "Mark's got himself a Grade A, blue ribbon, reserve champion brother. " Mark and William looked at each other, dazed, as though Doc had thrown two foreign words at them which they had trouble translating — "Son . . . brother" . . . William seemed to have lost the power of speech. His mouth kept opening but nothing came out.

Mark stood up and tested his weight on the bandaged foot. He had a real sensation of growing suddenly taller — like the shagmane mushrooms that sprouted up overnight along the corral fence.

Maybe his staying up all night with William and watching the sun come up for the first time had something to do with it. A thin wail came from the open upstairs window and Mark felt himself stretch up at least another inch.

Sabrina, sensing excitement, leaped from William's lap to Mark's shoulder. Mark put her down gently among the tree rubble.

"My pop and I have things to attend to," he said loftily. "You'd better go and look to your kittens, mind."

Scrapbook
Rudy Wiebe

In the darkness under the rafters he awoke to the screaming.

It was like his dream of being crushed by a huge tree and waking up to find his brother's arm lying on him, inert and solid in sleep. But now he had had no dream. Rather, he had felt something a long, long time, as if it stretched back without end into his slumber, even as if he had felt it forever: the leaping rise, the rasping plateau of sound, and then the moaning fall of it down to a whimper, before he awoke and heard it.

All was quiet for a moment after he awoke and these things groped through his thought, when suddenly he knew that David was not in bed beside him. Why wasn't he there? The strangeness of his absence and the sleep-remembered sound — had he heard something after he awoke? — welled fear in him. The straw-tick squeaking, he snuggled over into the big hollow and it was not warm at all. Where was David — *had* he heard — and then he jerked erect, careless of the dark, because the stove-pipe which reached up through the middle of the attic seemed surrounded by light. It was! for a light from below shone up through the opening around the pipe. Then he heard movement there. Were they all up, with the light burning? Perhaps he had heard —

The screaming came again. It occupied his bent body completely, that inhuman scream, as if he and it were alone in a universe; it drowned his brain until he could not hear it for the sound, and then it fell horribly, as if stretched beyond elasticity, down to a burbling moan.

He snatched the quilt up and over, but the half-warm darkness was not enough. He had to find them. His small bare feet were cold on the rough boards as, hunched against the darkness, he felt for the top of the ladder-like stairs near the oblong of grey that showed light below. Then he felt it and slipped down, feet quick on the familiar steps. The moaning had almost died now, and he could hear movement beyond the curtain of the living room. He crept over and pulled it aside.

He did not know what he saw as he stood for a long moment, fear forgotten. It was not that the lamp-light was strong on his sleep-rimmed eyes. Rather he did not know why his big sister Marg, who had lain on the bed in the corner of the living room for months because she had an enlarged heart, his mother said, was now in the middle of the night so stiffly erect in a chair, as if nailed there. And why David and his father should be holding her down. He had never seen her face like that. Like a crumpled paper-doll. Her black hair was stuck in strings over her forehead as his mother wiped her face, and then he saw the clothes-pin gripped in her teeth and the blood oozing from her lips. In the wonder of it he stared, rooted, and suddenly the pain within her tore the shell that held it and he heard the scream again, saw it ripped from her throat and saw the muscles of the men's arms bulge as they tried to hold her in the chair.

The fear numbed him now. He looked here and there as the sound seared him. If it was near David and his father, where — then he felt arms around him. His sister, five years older than himself, sitting crying by the door, clutched him to her.

It was not so long as last time, and he could look up as his father, face beaded with sweat and tears, said desperately, "Mother, we have to do something — we can't stand this," and David, almost maddened, hissing fiercely.

"Do something! *We* can't stand this! Look at her — thinking about yourself!"

And his mother, wiping the tortured face again, saying, "David, don't. That doesn't help. She bites her lips so much when she can't stand it — if we could only stop her burning. Maybe the Samsons — "

"Mrs. Samson would know *something* — get her — or do something. Get Bud to ride and get her."

They noticed him then as he huddled with his sobbing sister, not knowing himself what to do, cry or not. He didn't want to cry in front of David, who said crying was sissy, but Marg seemed to hurt so terribly. And everyone was so different. David said, "Bud, get Prince and ride for the Samsons. Quick!"

His mother bent over him. "I have to go out — I can't stay to see her — Toots, get some colder water and wipe her face. I'll take the lantern, Buddy."

In a rush he was dressed and out in the coolness where the spring frogs croaked hoarsely through the morning dark. He liked to ride, but now — when they were near the barn they heard the scream again but it seemed far away and unattached to him. Like a coyote howl in the night when he lay in bed. He jerked at the door, and the warmth from the horses moved around him. Straining, he reached up and looped the bridle off its peg. The only sound was the horses' breathing in the dark and his mother's half-held sobs as she raised the lantern in the doorway.

"Whoa," he said softly. "Easy, Prince, old boy," as he stroked the black object in the stall. The horse moved over, waking up, and he went into the narrow space murmuring quietly as David had taught him to do at night. The teeth would not open for a bit so he scrambled up on the manger and strained over to lever them apart, slipped the bridle over the flattened ears, snapped the strap, undid the halter shank and, grabbing the long mane, half swung, half jumped to the smooth back.

"Okay, Mom."

The light swung away and he backed the sleepy horse out of the stall, wheeled it, and, hanging over the left side, right arm and leg clinging, rode out the low door. He was glad he didn't have to walk out of the black barn.

"What shall I say, Mom? Mom?"

Her voice sounded choked. "Tell them Marg's terribly sick — to come quick and help."

Somehow her expression of those few words made him feel her dread for the first time. Someone, a neutral person, had to share this horrible night with them and he knew then he had to do something so he kicked the reluctant Prince sharply. As the horse moved he could hear her say, "Be careful, my little Buddy," and then her voice fell into prayer. He was so busy getting Prince into a gallop he did not hear the high distant sound reaching after him as he swung through the gate and onto the narrow road.

The clouds raced across the moon and its light flicked over the landscape as if whipped by a fierce wind. Down among the trees, however, all was still as he heard and felt the rhythmical clop of hooves carry up through him and into the night. With a shudder he knew he didn't like the spruce now. They were too solidly black. And grasping. He kicked Prince hard to get him past the muskeg. Where the moonlight slid out spasmodically, the violet blots of the spruce shadows leaped up and poured around him, and when there was no moon the darkness held all. The last stretch was an opaque tunnel, with the horse's withers rocking up at him, solid and living, in the (he knew abruptly) senseless fear that gripped him; just at the end the scream seemed to stab out of the blackness and he was terrified. But then he twisted the corner out of the forest to where poplars bordered the road on one side and the dull greyness of the Samson field stretched out against the pale, moving sky on the other.

The open was better; his thoughts raced on with the hard-running horse. This was like the dreams of riding through the night for help — all by himself, just as he had read in *Black Beauty*. Not many boys, perhaps not even most men, had ever done this. He'd tell them at school!

There was a clump of trees now, then the wooden bridge over a spring creek that burbled between sloughs filled with croaking frogs. The hoofs clunked hollow twice, and he was over, then in an instant saw the outline of the Samson gate. Prince turned up the lane. The farm-yard lay black and violet under the half-bare moon.

The dogs barked raucously out of their sleep as he slid off. Holding the reins taut, he banged on the door. "Mr. Samson! Mr. Samson!" Except for the dogs, he knew he could not have opened his mouth against the night. He hammered again and again, suddenly desperate for movement from the still house. Then, as he finally stopped for his numb fist and tilted over, panting, suddenly footsteps came. The door creaked.

"Mr. Samson—" he was staring at the long night-dress, "Mrs. — Marg's awful sick. Mom says, come quick, and help. . . ."

"What's wrong?"

"She — she (he did not know what to say) she bites herself and sits in the chair and David and Dad are holding onto her and — and — "

"Ride home quick, we'll come right away. George — " she was turning to the figure joining her in the lean-to.

He yanked Prince over to the wagon in the yard, scrambled up, jumped to his back and was headed home. He was cold now, and he saw the eastern tree-tops were just tipped, as with gold foil. Prince galloped with a will so he closed his eyes and hung on. The road was endless; the horse seemed to run so hard. He felt shaken apart and once he barely caught himself slipping off in sleep. He did not even see the spruce.

His mother was waiting, alone, in the yard. "She said they're coming, right away," he mumbled. He rode in, unsnapped the bridle, tumbled off, snapped the shank on and, dropping the bridle in the corner, went out. His mother took his arm at the door.

"I went in once, but it's too terrible. Oh my Buddy, she's burning up and I can't do anything. It came just like that — so quickly — and she's burning up!" They were near the woodpile and she dropped to her knees by the chopping block. He could feel her frantic clasp on his small body as she prayed, the same words over and over.

"Aw, Mom," he said when she choked, crying, "it's — "

He didn't know anything to say. Where was the word to say when his mother was like this. She who could do everything. Then his crying rose and fell with hers at the great unknowing fear, the helplessness he felt through her. The scream in the distance was very weak, and did not come again for a long time.

Suddenly a jingle of harness and, in a moment, the Samsons whirled up. As Mr. Samson tied the horse, Mrs. Samson came to them by the wood-pile and put her arm around his mother. She clutched his hand, sobbing, "She was getting so much better and all of a sudden, in the night—"

"We brought some laudanum — that should help some."

He knew it would be all right. They walked to the house; sleep kept pulling his head over as the house came closer. There was a dark door opening, closing them inside.

In the late morning when he awoke and came downstairs, his mother told him Margaret was dead.

The house did not smell right. Everyone seemed to be struck dumb, and cried unexpectedly. He could not find David anywhere. He did not want to go into the living room; he could not think of anyone as dead.

"Mom," he said, "I want to go to school."

His mother didn't seem to hear him. After she had told him she had turned away and was washing dishes, alone in her grief for the girl she had nursed so long.

He went out, and the early spring sunshine was fresh and good. No one noticed him as he slipped into the barn, bridled Prince, and rode off.

Yet, somehow, school wasn't right either. When he got there he didn't feel like saying anything about his ride, or even why he arrived during recess. He sat at his small desk in the one-room school and the teacher said, "Grade three, take out your Healthy Foods Scrapbooks." He opened his desk and there, slightly dog-eared and crumpled from much looking, lay the scrapbook. He and Marg had made it for health class. Actually Marg had done all the work; he had just watched. That was why his book had been first in class. On the cover was the bulging red tomato she had cut from the tomato-juice label, and there was the kink she had made when he bumped her because he was leaning so close as she sat propped in bed, cutting it out. He said, almost aloud, "She's dead," and he knew that 'dead' was like the sticks of rabbits he found in his snares.

And suddenly he began to cry. Everyone stared, but he could not stop.

Generations

Teddy at Kispiox Village
Michael G. Coleman

Shattered sunlight spills across white snows
at Kispiox. We squint to shield our eyes
from blinding crystal-brilliance of the glare
under blue and cloudless northern skies.
We stand near where a winding river flows
and watch soft smoke from winter waters rise
the breath of myths. Clean cold December air
sparkles around the village totem poles.
My son, a vital, fearless three-year-old,
seems strangely silent under the stern stare
of winter-weathered wood. At last he sighs.
Perhaps he senses, as I do, the care
an ancient artist took to carve and mould
such culture-guarding sentinels, shadows
that bind a mute mist-shrouded past. Wise
witnesses in snow, both bold and bare
they stand, impassive signs of spirit-souls
at timeless Kispiox. And Teddy knows.

To Set Our House in Order
Margaret Laurence

When the baby was almost ready to be born, something went wrong and my mother had to go to the hospital two weeks before the expected time. I was awakened by her crying in the night, and then I heard my father's footsteps as he went downstairs to phone. I stood in the doorway of my room, shivering and listening, wanting to go to my mother, but afraid to go lest there be some sight there more terrifying than I could bear.

"Hello, Paul?" my father said, and I knew he was talking to Doctor Cates. "It's Beth. I'm only thinking of what happened the last time, and another like that would be — Yes, I think that would be the best thing. Okay, make it as soon as you can."

He came back upstairs, looking bony and dishevelled in his pyjamas, and running his fingers through his sand-coloured hair. At the top of the stairs he came face to face with Grandmother MacLeod, who was standing there in her quilted black-satin dressing gown, her light figure held straight and poised, as though she was unaware that her hair was bound grotesquely like white-feathered wings in the snare of her coarse night-time hairnet.

"What is it, Ewen?"

"It's all right, Mother. Beth's having . . . a little trouble. I'm going to take her to the hospital. You go back to bed."

"I told you," Grandmother MacLeod said in her clear voice, never loud, but distinct and ringing like the tap of a silver spoon on a crystal goblet, "I did tell you, Ewen, did I not, that you should have got a girl in to help her with the housework? She should have rested more."

"I couldn't afford to get anyone in," my father said. "If you thought she should've rested more, why didn't you ever . . . Oh

God, I'm out of my mind tonight. Just go back to bed, Mother, please. I must get back to Beth."

When my father went down to open the front door for Doctor Cates, my need overcame my fear and I slipped into my parents' room. My mother's black hair, so neatly pinned up during the day, was startlingly spread across the white pillowcase. I stared at her, not speaking, and then she smiled, and I rushed from the doorway and buried my head upon her.

"It's all right, Vanessa," she said. "Honey, the baby's just going to come a little early, that's all. You'll be all right. Grandmother MacLeod will be here."

"How can she get the meals?" I wailed, fixing on the first thing that came to mind. "She never cooks. She doesn't know how."

"Yes, she does," my mother said. "She can cook as well as anyone when she has to. She's just never had to very much, that's all. Don't worry, she'll keep everything in order, and then some."

My father and Doctor Cates came in, and I had to go, without saying anything I had wanted to say. I went back to my own room and lay with the shadows all around me, listening to the night murmurings that always went on in that house, sounds that never had a source — rafters and beams contracting in the dry air, perhaps, or mice in the walls, or a sparrow that had flown into the attic through the broken skylight there. After a while, although I would not have believed it possible, I slept.

The next morning, though summer vacation was not quite over, I did not feel like going out to play with any of the kids. I was very superstitious and felt that if I left the house, even for a few hours, some disaster would overtake my mother. I did not, of course, mention this to Grandmother MacLeod, for she did not believe in the existence of fear, or if she did, she never let on.

I spent the morning morbidly, seeking hidden places in the house. There were many of these — odd-shaped nooks under the stairs, and dusty tunnels and forgotten recesses in the heart of the house where the only things actually to be seen were drab oil paintings stacked upon the rafters and trunks full of outmoded clothing and old photograph albums. But the unseen presences in these secret places I knew to be those of every person, young or old, who had ever belonged to the house and had died, including Uncle Roderick who got killed on the Somme and the baby who would have been my sister if only she had come to life. Grandfather MacLeod, who had died a year after I was born, was present in the house in more tangible form. At the top of the main stairs hung a mammoth picture of a darkly uniformed man riding a horse whose prancing stance and dilated nostrils suggested the battle was not yet over, that it might continue until Judgment Day. The stern man was the Duke of Wellington, but at the time I believed him to be my Grandfather MacLeod, still keeping an eye on things.

We had moved in with Grandmother MacLeod when the depression got bad and she could no longer afford a housekeeper; yet the MacLeod house never seemed like home to me. Its dark-red brick was grown over at the front with Virginia creeper that turned crimson in the fall until you could hardly tell brick from leaves. It boasted a small tower in which Grandmother MacLeod kept a weed-like collection of anaemic ferns. The veranda was embellished with a profusion of wrought-iron scrolls, and the circular rose window upstairs contained many-coloured glass that permitted an outlooking eye to see the world as a place of absolute sapphire or emerald or, if one wished to look with a jaundiced eye, a hateful yellow. In Grandmother MacLeod's opinion, these features gave the house style. To me, they seemed fascinating, but rather as the paraphernalia of an alchemist's laboratory might be, things to be peered at curiously but with caution, just in case.

Inside, a multitude of doors led to rooms where my presence, if not actually forbidden, was not encouraged. One was Grandmother MacLeod's bedroom, with its stale and old-smelling reek of medicines and lavender sachets. Here resided her monogrammed dresser silver — brush and mirror, nail buffer and button hook and scissors — none of which must even be fingered by me now, for she meant to leave them to me in her will and intended to hand them over in their original flawless and unused condition. Here, too, were the silver-framed photographs of Uncle Roderick — as a child, as a boy, as a man in army uniform. The massive walnut spool bed had obviously been designed for queens or giants, and my tiny grandmother used to lie within it all day when she had migraines, contriving somehow to look like a giant queen.

The day my mother went to the hospital, Grandmother MacLeod called me at lunch-time, and when I appeared, smudged with dust from the attic, she looked at me distastefully.

"For mercy's sake, Vanessa, what have you been doing with yourself? Get washed this minute. Not that way. Use the back stairs, young lady. Get along now. Oh, your father phoned."

I swung around. "What did he say? How is she? Is the baby born?"

"Curiosity killed the cat," Grandmother MacLeod said, frowning. "I cannot understand Beth and Ewen telling you all these things at your age. What sort of vulgar person you'll grow up to be, I dare not think. No, it's not born yet. Your mother's just the same. No change."

I looked at my grandmother, not wanting to appeal to her, but unable to stop myself. "Will she — will she be all right?"

Grandmother MacLeod straightened her already straight back. "If I said definitely yes, Vanessa, that would be a lie, and the MacLeods do not tell lies, as I have tried to impress upon you before. What happens is God's will. 'The Lord giveth, and the Lord taketh away.' "

Appalled, I turned away so that she would not see my face. Surprisingly, I heard her sigh and felt her papery white and perfectly manicured hand upon my shoulder.

"When your Uncle Roderick got killed," she said, "I thought I would die. But I didn't die, Vanessa."

At lunch she chatted animatedly, and I realized she was trying to cheer me in the only way she knew. "When I married your Grandfather MacLeod, he said to me, 'Eleanor, don't think because we're going to the prairies that I expect you to live roughly. You're used to a proper house, and you shall have one.' He was as good as his word. Before we'd been in Manawaka three years, he'd had this place built. He earned a good deal of money in his time, your grandfather. He soon had more patients than either of the other doctors. We ordered our dinner service and all our silver from Birks in Toronto. We had resident help in those days, of course, and never had less than twelve guests for dinner parties. When I had a tea, it would always be twenty or thirty. Never any less than half a dozen different kinds of cake were ever served in this house. Well, no one seems to bother much these days. Too lazy, I suppose."

"Too broke," I suggested. "That's what Dad says."

"I can't bear slang," Grandmother MacLeod said. "If you mean hard up, why don't you say so? It's mainly a question of management, anyway. My accounts were always in good order, and so was my house. No unexpected expenses that couldn't be met, no fruit cellar running out of preserves before the winter was over. Do you know what my father used to say to me when I was a girl?"

"No," I said. "What?"

" 'God loves order,' " Grandmother MacLeod replied with emphasis. "You remember that, Vanessa, 'God loves order.' He wants each one of us to set our house in order. I've never forgotten those words of my father's. I was a MacInnes before I got married. The MacInnes is a very ancient clan, the lairds of Morven and the constables of the Castle of Kinlochaline. Did you finish that book I gave you?"

"Yes," I said. Then, feeling additional comment was called for, I added, "It was a swell book, Grandmother."

This was somewhat short of the truth. I had been hoping for her cairngorm brooch on my tenth birthday and had received instead the plaid-bound volume entitled *The Clans and Tartans of Scotland.* Most of it was too boring to read, but I had looked up the motto of my own family and those of some of my friends' families. *Be then a wall of brass. Learn to suffer. Consider the end. Go carefully.* I had not found any of these slogans reassuring. What with Mavis Duncan learning to suffer, and Laura Kennedy considering the end, and Patsy Drummond going carefully, and I spending my time in being a wall of brass, it did not seem to me that any of us were going to lead very interesting lives. I did not say this to Grandmother MacLeod.

"The MacInnes motto is *Pleasure arises from work,*" I said.

"Yes," she agreed proudly. "And an excellent motto it is, too. One to bear in mind."

She rose from the table, rearranging on her bosom the looped ivory beads that held the pendant on which a full-blown ivory rose was stiffly carved.

"I hope Ewen will be pleased," she said.

"What at?"

"Didn't I tell you?" Grandmother MacLeod said. "I hired a girl this morning for the housework. She's to start tomorrow."

When my father got home that evening, Grandmother MacLeod told him her good news. He ran a hand distractedly across his forehead.

"I'm sorry, Mother, but you'll just have to unhire her. I can't possibly pay anyone."

"It seems odd," Grandmother MacLeod snapped, "that you can afford to eat chicken four times a week."

"Those chickens," my father said in an exasperated voice, "are how people are paying their bills. The same with the eggs and the milk. That scrawny turkey that arrived yesterday was for Logan MacCardney's appendix, if you must know. We probably eat better than any family in Manawaka, except Niall Cameron's. People can't entirely dispense with doctors or undertakers. That doesn't mean to say I've got any cash. Look, Mother, I don't know what's happening with Beth. Paul thinks he may have to do a Caesarean. Can't we leave all this? Just leave the house alone. Don't touch it. What does it matter?"

"I have never lived in a messy house, Ewen," Grandmother MacLeod said, "and I don't intend to begin now."

"Oh, Lord," my father said. "Well, I'll phone Edna, I guess, and see if she can give us a hand, although God knows she's got enough, with the Connor house and her parents to look after."

"I don't fancy having Edna Connor in to help," Grandmother MacLeod said.

"Why not." my father shouted. "She's Beth's sister, isn't she?"

"She speaks in such a slangy way," Grandmother MacLeod said. "I have never believed she was a good influence on Vanessa. And there is no need for you to raise your voice to me, Ewen, if you please."

I could barely control my rage. I thought my father would surely rise to Aunt Edna's defence. But he did not.

"It'll be all right," he soothed her. "She'd only be here for part of the day, Mother. You could stay in your room."

Aunt Edna strode in the next morning. The sight of her bobbed black hair and her grin made me feel better at once. She hauled out the carpet sweeper and the weighted polisher and got to work. I dusted while she polished and swept, and we got through the living room and front hall in next to no time.

"Where's her royal highness, kiddo?" she inquired.

"In her room," I said. "She's reading the catalogue from Robinson and Cleaver."

"Good glory, not again?" Aunt Edna cried. "The last time she ordered three linen tea cloths and two dozen napkins. It came to fourteen dollars. Your mother was absolutely frantic. I guess I shouldn't be saying this."

"I knew anyway," I assured her. "She was at the lace-handkerchief section when I took up her coffee."

"Let's hope she stays there. Heaven forbid she should get onto the banqueting cloths. Well, at least she believes the Irish are good for two things — manual labour and linen-making. She's never forgotten Father used to be a blacksmith, before he got the hardware store. Can you beat it? I wish it didn't bother Beth."

"Does it?" I asked and immediately realized this was a wrong move, for Aunt Edna was suddenly scrutinizing me.

"We're making you grow up before your time," she said. "Don't pay any attention to me, Nessa. I must've got up on the wrong side of the bed this morning."

But I was unwilling the leave the subject. "All the same," I said thoughtfully, "Grandmother MacLeod's family were the lairds of Morven and the constables of the Castle of Kinlochaline. I bet you didn't know that."

Aunt Edna snorted. "Castle, my foot. She was born in Ontario, just like your Grandfather Connor, and her father was a horse doctor. Come on, kiddo, we'd better shut up and get down to business here."

We worked in silence for a while.

"Aunt Edna," I said at last, "what about Mother? Why won't they let me go and see her?"

"Kids aren't allowed to visit maternity patients. It's tough for you, I know. Look, Nessa, don't worry. If it doesn't start tonight, they're going to do the operation. She's getting the best of care."

I stood there, holding the feather duster like a dead bird in my hands. I was not aware that I was going to speak until the words came out. "I'm scared," I said.

Aunt Edna put her arms around me, and her face looked all at once stricken and empty of defences.

"Oh, honey, I'm scared, too," she said.

It was this way that Grandmother MacLeod found us when she came stepping lightly down into the front hall with her order for two dozen lace-bordered handkerchiefs of pure Irish linen.

I could not sleep that night, and when I went downstairs, I found my father in the den. I sat down on the hassock beside his chair, and he told me about the operation my mother was to have the next morning. He kept saying it was not serious nowadays.

"But you're worried," I put in, as though seeking to explain why I was.

"I should at least have been able to keep from burdening you with it," he said in a distant voice, as though to himself. "If only the baby hadn't got twisted around —"

"Will it be born dead, like the little girl?"

"I don't know," my father said. "I hope not."

"She'd be disappointed, wouldn't she, if it was?" I said, wondering why I was not enough for her.

"Yes, she would," my father replied. "She won't be able to have any more, after this. It's partly on your account that she wants this one, Nessa. She doesn't want you to grow up without a brother or sister."

"As far as I'm concerned, she didn't need to bother."

My father laughed. "Well, let's talk about something else, and then maybe you'll be able to sleep. How did you and Grandmother make out today?"

"Oh, fine, I guess. What was Grandfather MacLeod like, Dad?"

"What did she tell you about him?"

"She said he made a lot of money in his time."

"Well, he wasn't any millionaire," my father said, "but I suppose he did quite well. That's not what I associate with him, though." He reached across to the bookshelf, took out a small leather-bound volume and opened it. On the pages were mysterious marks, like doodling, only much neater and more patterned.

"What is it?" I asked.

"Greek," my father explained. "this is a play called *Antigone.* See, here's the title in English. There's a whole stack of them on the shelves there. *Oedipus Rex, Electra, Medea,* They belonged to your Grandfather MacLeod. He used to read them often."

"Why?" I inquired, unable to understand why anyone would pore over those undecipherable signs.

"He was interested in them," my father said. "He must have been a lonely man, although it never struck me that way at the time. Sometimes a thing only hits you a long time afterward."

"Why would he be lonely?" I wanted to know.

"He was the only person in Manawaka who could read these plays in the original Greek," my father said. "I don't suppose many people, if anyone, had even read them in English translation. Maybe he once wanted to be a classical scholar — I don't know. But his father was a doctor, so that's what he was. Maybe he would have liked to talk to somebody about these plays. They must have meant a lot to him."

It seemed to me that my father was talking oddly. There was a sadness in his voice that I had never heard before, and I longed to say something that would make him feel better, but I could not, because I did not know what was the matter.

"Can you read this kind of writing?" I asked hesitantly.

My father shook his head. "Nope. I was never very intellectual, I guess. Your Uncle Rod was always brighter than I in school, but even he wasn't interested in learning Greek. Perhaps he would've been later, if he'd lived. As a kid, all I ever wanted to do was go into the merchant marine."

"Why didn't you?"

"Oh, well," my father said, "a kid who'd never seen the sea wouldn't have made much of a sailor. I might have turned out to be the seasick type."

I had lost interest, now that he was once more speaking like himself.

"Grandmother MacLeod was pretty cross today about the girl," I said.

"I know," my father said. 'Well, we must be as nice as we can to her, Nessa, and after a while she'll be all right."

Suddenly I did not care what I said. "Why can't she be nice to *us* for a change?" I burst out. "We're always the ones who have to be nice to her."

My father put his hand down and tilted my head until I was forced to look at him. "Vanessa," he said, "she's had troubles in her life which you really don't know much about. That's why she sometimes gets migraines and has to go to bed. It's not easy for her these days. The house is still the same, so she thinks other things should be, too. It hurts her when she finds they aren't."

"I don't see — " I began.

"Listen," my father said, "you know we were talking just now about what people are interested in, like Grandfather MacLeod being interested in Greek plays? Well, your grandmother was interested in being a lady, Nessa, and for a long time it seemed to her that she was one."

I thought of the Castle of Kinlochaline and of horse doctors in Ontario.

"I didn't know — " I stammered.

"That's usually the trouble with most of us," my father said. "Now go on up to bed. I'll phone tomorrow from the hospital as soon as the operation's over."

I did sleep at last, and in my dreams I could hear the caught sparrow fluttering in the attic and the sound of my mother crying and the voices of dead children.

My father did not phone until afternoon. Although

Grandmother MacLeod said I was being silly, for you could hear the phone ringing all over the house, I refused to move out of the den. I had never before examined my father's books, but now, at a loss for something to do, I took them out one by one and read snatches here and there. After several hours, it dawned on me that most of the books were of the same kind. I looked again at the titles.

Seven League Boots, Travels in Arabia, Deserta, The Seven Pillars of Wisdom, Travels in Tartary, Thibet and China, Count Luckner, The Sea Devil. And a hundred more. On a shelf by themselves were copies of *National Geographic Magazine.* I had looked at these often enough, but never with the puzzling compulsion which I felt now, as though I was on the verge of some discovery, something which I had to find out and yet did not want to know. I riffled through the picture-filled pages. Hibiscus and wild orchids grew in soft-petaled profusion. The Himalayas stood loftily as gods, with the morning sun on their peaks of snow. Leopards snarled from the depth of a thousand jungles. Schooners buffeted their white sails like the wings of giant angels against the sea winds.

"What on earth are you doing?" Grandmother MacLeod inquired waspishly, from the doorway. "You've got everything scattered all over the place. Pick it all up this minute, Vanessa, do you hear?" So I picked up the books and magazines and put them neatly away.

When the telephone finally rang, I was afraid to answer it. At last I did. My father sounded far away, and the relief in his voice made it unsteady.

"It's okay, honey. Everything's fine. The boy was born alive and kicking after all. Your mother's pretty weak, but she's going to be all right."

I could hardly believe it. I did not want to talk to anyone. I wanted to be by myself, to assimilate the presence of my brother, toward whom, without even having seen him, I felt such tenderness and such resentment.

That evening, Grandmother MacLeod approached my father, who at first did not take her seriously when she asked what they planned to call the child.

"Oh, I don't know. Hank, maybe, or Joe. Fauntleroy, perhaps."

She ignored his levity. "Ewen, I wish you would call him Roderick."

His face changed. "I'd rather not."

"I think you should," Grandmother MacLeod insisted, in a voice as pointed and precise as her silver nail scissors.

"Don't you think Beth ought to decide?" my father asked.

"Beth will agree if you do."

My father did not bother to deny something that even I knew to be true. He did not say anything. Then Grandmother MacLeod's voice, astonishingly, faltered a little. "It would mean a great deal to me," she said.

I remembered what she had told me — *When your Uncle Roderick got killed, I thought I would die. But I didn't die.* All at once her feeling for that unknown dead man became a reality for me. And yet I held it against her, as well, for I could see that she was going to win now.

"All right," my father said. "We'll call him Roderick."

Then, alarmingly, he threw back his head and laughed. "Roderick Dhu!" he cried. "That's what you'll call him, isn't it? Black Roderick. Like before. Don't you remember? As though he was a character out of Sir Walter Scott, instead of an ordinary kid who — "

He broke off and looked at her with a kind of desolation in his face.

"God, I'm sorry, Mother," he said. "I had no right to say that."

Grandmother MacLeod did not flinch, or tremble, or indicate that she felt anything at all. "I accept your apology, Ewen," she said.

My mother had to stay in bed for several weeks after she

arrived home. The baby's crib was kept in my parents' room, and I could go in and look at the small creature who lay there with his tightly closed fists and his feathery black hair. Aunt Edna came in to help each morning, and when she had finished the housework, she would have coffee with my mother. They kept the door closed, but this did not prevent me from eavesdropping, for there was an air register in the floor of the spare room that was linked somehow with the register in my parents' room. If you put your ear to the iron grille, it was almost like a radio.

"Did you mind very much, Beth?" Aunt Edna was saying.

"Oh, it's not the name I mind," my mother replied. "It's just that Ewen felt he had to. You know that Rod only had the sight of one eye, didn't you?"

"Sure, I knew. So what?"

"There was only a year and a half between Ewen and Rod," my mother said, "so they often went around together when they were youngsters. It was Ewen's air rifle that did it."

"Oh, Lord," Aunt Edna said. "I suppose she always blamed him?"

"No, I don't think it was so much that, really. It was how he felt himself. I think he even used to wonder sometimes if — but people shouldn't let themselves think like that, or they'd go crazy. Accidents do happen, after all. When the war came, Ewen joined up first. Rod should never have been in the army at all, but he couldn't wait to get in. He must have lied about his eyesight. It wasn't so very noticeable unless you looked at him closely, and I don't suppose the medicals were very thorough in those days. He got in as a gunner, and Ewen applied to have him in the same company. He thought he might be able to watch out for him, I guess, Rod being at a disadvantage. They were both only kids. Ewen was nineteen and Rod was eighteen when they went to France. And then the Somme. I don't know, Edna, I think Ewen felt that if Rod had had proper sight, or if he hadn't been in the same outfit and had been sent somewhere else — you know how people always think these things afterward, not that it's ever a bit of use. Ewen wasn't there when Rod got hit. They'd lost each other somehow, and Ewen was looking for him, not bothering about anything else, you know, just frantically looking. Then he stumbled across him quite by chance. Rod was still alive, but —"

"Stop it, Beth," Aunt Edna said. "You're only upsetting yourself."

"Ewen never spoke of it to me," my mother went on, "until his mother showed me the letter he'd written to her at the time. It was a peculiar letter, almost formal, saying how gallantly Rod had died, and all that. I guess I shouldn't have, but I told him she'd shown it to me. He was very angry that she had. And then, as though for some reason he was terribly ashamed, he said 'I had to write something to her, but men don't really die like that, Beth. It wasn't that way at all.' It was only after the war that he decided to study medicine and go into practice with his father."

"Had Rod meant to?" Aunt Edna asked.

"I don't know," my mother said. "I never felt I should ask Ewen that."

Aunt Edna was gathering up the coffee things, for I could hear the clash of cups and saucers being stacked on the tray. "You know what I heard her say to Vanessa once, Beth? 'The MacLeods never tell lies.' Those were her exact words. Even then, I didn't know whether to laugh or cry."

"Please, Edna." My mother sounded worn out now. "Don't."

"Oh, glory," Aunt Edna said, "I've got all the delicacy of a two-ton truck. I didn't mean Ewen, for heaven's sake. That wasn't what I meant at all. Here, let me plump up your pillows for you."

Then the baby began to cry, so I could not hear anything more of interest. I took my bike and went out beyond

Manawaka, riding aimlessly along the gravel highway. It was late summer, and the wheat had changed colour, but instead of being high and bronzed in the fields, it was stunted and desiccated, for there had been no rain again this year. Yet on the bluff where I stopped and crawled under the barbed-wire fence and lay stretched out on the grass, the plentiful poplar leaves were turning to a luminous yellow and shone like church windows in the sun. I put my head down very close to the earth and looked at what was going on there. Grasshoppers with enormous eyes ticked and twitched around me, as though the dry air was perfect for their purposes. A ladybug laboured mightily to climb a blade of grass, fell off and started all over again, seeming to be unaware that she possessed wings and could have flown up.

I thought of the accidents that might easily happen to a person — or, of course, might not happen, might happen to somebody else. I thought of the dead baby, my sister, who might as easily have been I. Would she, then, have been lying here in my place, the sharp grass making its small toothmarks on her brown arms, the sun warming her to the heart? I thought of the leather-bound volumes of Greek, and of the six different kinds of iced cakes that used to be offered always in the MacLeod house, and of the pictures of leopards and green seas. I thought of my brother, who had been born alive after all, and now had been given his life's name.

I could not really comprehend these things, but I sensed their strangeness, their disarray. I felt that whatever God might love in this world, it was certainly not order.

Damian

Amy Marie George

Damian darling,
son of mine
joy and happiness of life,
light of my cloudy days
and nights.
Little toddler so sweet, small
yet so strong
with such power
how can I endure this pain of partedness
with the squeals of your delight
still echoing through these still
silent walls
tearing
burning
hurting
this mother's heart of mine.
Oh, baby son of mine
how did I spend the hours
before you came to me
and where was I
when I was not with you.
Now, as I sit
this ache within my breast
waiting
hoping for that peaceful moment when,
once more
I hold your baby's flesh
to me again
and flow this love
welded up inside of me
into your own heart.

The Night Grandma Died
Elizabeth Brewster

"Here's Grandmother in here," Cousin Joy said,
Standing beside me at the bedroom door,
One hand on my shoulder. "You see, she's only sleeping."
But I, nine years old and frightened,
Knew it was a lie. Grandmother's shell
Lay on the bed, hands folded, head on one side.
The spirit that had groaned so loud an hour ago
Gone out of her. I looked, and turned and ran,
First to the kitchen. There were the aunts
Who had laid her out, still weeping
Over a good hot cup of tea: Aunt Stella,
Large, dominant; Aunt Alice, a plump, ruffled hen of a
    woman;
My small, quick mother; Aunt Grace, youngest and shyest,
Awkward on the edge of the group: "Shush," she was saying
To Cousin Pauline, who was lying on the floor
Pretending to be Grandma.

And they all got up and came into the parlour,
Where suddenly everyone was jovial,
And Aunt April sat in the best chair
Nursing her newest baby,
And the uncles sat talking of crops and weather,
And Uncle Harry, who had come from Maine,
Pumped the hands of people he hadn't seen in twenty years,
And Grandma's nephew Eh from up the road
Played everybody's favourite tune on the piano.
Now and then, remembering the corpse, he burst into a Baptist
    hymn,
His rich bass voice, dark and deep as molasses,
Flowing protectively over the women,
While his eyes, also dark,

Wrapped them warm with sympathy.
And I, sitting on a footstool in a corner,
Was sometimes warmed by the voice,
And sometimes chilled remembering
In the room next door
Grandmother, dead, whom I had never liked.

My Grandfather
Richard Chief Calf

My Grandfather who used to walk
Up and down the hills and roads
And creeks and banks
Skin was brown,
Hair was white with bits of black,
And a bag of tobacco he carried around.
He looked at the brush,
He looked at the hill,
By the stream that runs in the coolee
Is where he sits,
But now he lies to rest in peace.
O Grandfather!
  I still see you
    On the top of the hill
      In my dreams.

Some People's Grandfathers
Gwen Pharis Ringwood

The boy and the old man started out early to look at the
trapline. They took some bread and dried salmon to eat along
the trail.

  The boy, Little Joe, wanted to go fishing with the other

Indians but he had no choice. Whenever his grandfather, Old Joe, went anywhere Little Joe was expected to go along.

"The old man don't see so good," Sammy Jacob would say to his son, "You go with him. Watch he don't fall over the cliff."

Since the trail to the trapline went nowhere near a cliff, Little Joe thought this a very stupid admonition. He looked at his father every time to see if Sammy Jacob was making a joke but Sammy's face remained flat as a stone.

If Old Joe acted like some grandfathers, I wouldn't mind, Little Joe told himself. Some grandfathers made jokes, and told stories, and gave their grandsons cigarettes to smoke. But not Old Joe! When he talked, he ordered. "Get this. Do that. Have respect." When he wasn't ordering, Old Joe stomped along in silence.

To make it worse, Old Joe always carried the gun. Little Joe would bring out the rifle, but right away the old man would say, "I better take the gun. We might see something." Every time. When they did come on something, Old Joe often missed, not being able to see so good. Last year he had shot a buck all right, a six-pointer, but Little Joe put this down to accident.

So here they were on a winter morning trudging through snow and deadfall, with Old Joe, silent as a bird dog, carrying the gun as usual, and Little Joe, with only one mitten, because his sister had lost the other one, walking ahead and holding the branches back so they wouldn't slap the old man in the face.

Over on the lake Sammy Jacob and Bob and Bob's two boys were fishing through the ice. There would be a big fire and a big lunch and everybody would be telling stories and jokes. Likely Little Joe's stuck-up cousins were drinking tea and smoking and pulling ling out of the lake like crazy. The way Little Joe saw it, Old Joe had lived too long. Eighty years is too long, reasoned Little Joe. Why, Old Joe still wore buckskin moccasins and his idea of a big day was to go berry picking down by the river.

Sammy Jacob said Old Joe had been a great bronc rider but that must have been about 100 years ago. The only horses he had anything to do with now were the old pintos he drove down the river when the salmon were running. The rest of the time Old Joe stayed around the camp giving orders. Whenever something exciting was going on like fishing through the ice, then Old Joe decided to visit the trapline.

Sometimes Little Joe didn't know how he stood it, bodyguarding Old Joe, day in and day out, since he could remember. Why, he had even had to stay home from the stampede last year to look after Old Joe because the old man didn't feel like riding 50 miles in a wagon! No doubt about it, Old Joe had lived too long.

"Now I'm 11 years old, maybe I could carry the gun," Little Joe said as they started.

"Ah, it gets heavy," the old man said. "Besides, we might see something."

Old Joe didn't speak again until they reached the first trap which was sprung but empty. "Wolf," he said, examining the tracks.

As if a person wouldn't know a wolf track.

They cut through heavy timber. "If you get lost, boy, build a fire against a big log like this one. Make a shelter of spruce boughs. A man can stay alive a long time, if he's warm."

"I don't get lost," said Little Joe.

"In a storm anybody can get lost. Have respect." Old Joe spoke crossly, shaking Little Joe by the shoulder.

Little Joe stuck his tongue out but he was careful the old man didn't see. Little Joe was hungry but there was no use suggesting they eat until they'd checked the second trap.

They came out on a clearing. "Moose," Little Joe hissed.

The big moose was browsing on the far side of the clearing. As he raised his head, the massive fluted shells of his antlers were oulined against the gray sky. He was grotesque but impressive. His great bulk was supported on thin steel-muscled legs. His shaggy beard and overhanging upper lip looked strange and ugly beneath the magnificent antlers.

Old Joe levered a shell into the rifle. He motioned Little Joe behind. The boy longed to grab the rifle but he obeyed.

The old man fired. The moose shuddered, blood spurted from his neck, but he did not fall. Old Joe reloaded. His second shot was high.

"Look out," Little Joe shouted. As he yelled, the moose charged across the clearing.

Little Joe saw the moose lift his grandfather in the air and drop him sprawling on the ground, saw the moose run on and turn, grunting angrily. The terrible front feet were braced for a second charge. The rifle lay a few feet from Old Joe's inert form.

Little Joe looked at a pile of logs to his left in the middle of the clearing. Could he make it? He must try.

He must try now! The moose was running again towards Old Joe.

The boy ran out yelling and waving his cap. "Yaa . . . ! Ya . . . ! Yaaa . . . !" he shouted. The moose stopped, turned towards this new enemy, "Yaaa . . . ! Ya . . . !" Little Joe taunted, as he ran. The deadly feet pounded behind him. The boy threw himself under the deadfall, close to the wedged poplar logs. The bull vaulted the logs, ran a few feet and turned.

Little Joe knew the moose, enraged by its wound, would continue to charge until he had cut the old man to ribbons, unless the animal's attention could be diverted. The bull was once more eyeing Old Joe.

Again and again Little Joe forced himself through the dangerous manoeuvre. He would run out from the deadfall, attract the moose, flee from the lowered antlers and the pounding forefeet, until he could roll under the logs. The bull pawed and bunted at the sheltering poplars, and blood from the wound spurted out onto the logs and onto Little Joe's clothes.

Once the old man moved. He was alive after all!

"Stay down," Little Joe shouted, "Don't move." The old man lay still but the moose had seen him move and headed toward him.

This time Little Joe had to run about 30 feet from the deadfall to deflect the moose's charge. The cruel front feet missed him by inches as he ran under the logs. How long could the moose bleed so? The snow in the clearing was stained with blood and yet the bull showed no signs of weakening.

"See me, Old Moose? See me?" Little Joe stumbled but ran on. He wasn't going to make it this time. He couldn't! He looked back frantically. Suddenly the moose stopped. The proud head wavered, the front legs buckled and the great body crashed down, rolled, shuddered and lay still in the bloodstained snow.

Little Joe felt relief and awe and pity as he circled the body of his enemy. Then he ran to Old Joe. "He's dead. Your bullet got him."

Old Joe didn't move.

"Are you hurt bad?" Little Joe begged for an answer. Eighty years was too soon to die, 80 years wasn't enough for the tall black-haired old man who always tried to pull his weight in camp. Why, 80 years was just the age a grandfather should be!

Old Joe turned his head. A gash furrowed the leathered cheek, the left eye was swollen shut, the skin bruised and purple.

"I thought you were dead," Little Joe smiled.

"I think my shoulder is broken maybe. Lift on my right side." Little Joe obeyed. Finally they stood together looking at the clearing. "Some moose," Old Joe said.

Little Joe picked up the rifle, "We can come back for him."

A wet sleety snow was falling as they walked the trail home. When the cabin came into view, Sammy Jacob and the others were skinning ling outside. Little Joe's mother looked up first. Then they all stared until Sammy Jacob ran jerkily up the hill shouting "What happened?"

Only then did Little Joe realize what a fearful sight they made, two blood-soaked apparitions moving through the falling snow. "A moose hurt my grandfather," shouted Little Joe.

After they got the old man in bed, after Little Joe changed his clothes and ate something, after they had gone back to the clearing, skinned the moose, hung the meat, stretched the hide, dragged home the five-foot antlers, then they all sat around the stove drinking tea and talking.

Bob lit a tailormade and put it in Old Joe's mouth, then he passed the pack to Sammy Jacob and the cousins. They all lit up. Then Bob offered a cigarette to Little Joe.

"I don't smoke," Little Joe mumbled. His ears couldn't believe his own mouth was talking. He had waited for years for them to offer him cigarettes to smoke. His cousins grinned and whispered. They thought he was chicken. Little Joe hunched down miserably on the floor.

They were talking about the moose. He wished he could tell them how the moose had looked — as proud as a tall spruce, as angry as the lightning, but he couldn't tell them.

"Some moose," Sammy Jacob said.

Old Joe's one good eye looked straight ahead. His swollen face twisted into a grisly grin. "Some man," he said. But Little Joe didn't hear. Little Joe's head dropped against the log wall and he slept.

It wasn't long before Old Joe felt better. One morning he moved stiffly out to sniff the sunlight. Water rippled down the hills into the creek, the creek tumbled down to the river. Light green feathers tipped the pine trees. The squirrels darted up and down the tree trunks, teasing the dogs.

Sammy Jacob and his brother Bob were getting ready to round up horses.

"I think we should look at the traps today," Old Joe said, looking at Little Joe. Sammy Jacob started to speak and then shut up his mouth. Little Joe went in for the rifle. He offered it to his grandfather.

"You better carry the gun," Old Joe ordered. "We might see something."

Little Joe, silent as a bird dog, carried the rifle along the trail. He walked a little ahead of Old Joe and was careful to hold back the branches so they wouldn't slap the old man.

The Last Rose
Sheryl Brown

A coral red rose from Mama's garden.
      The Last Rose.
— snow glistened and spread like
      a glorious winter blanket
hushed are the sounds — aroma
      from yesterday's autumn breeze.
The green grass and sweet smells
      have faded — our cosy haven with Mama's touch
        made strange feelings intimate
So as a young girl she was —
      The Last Rose
      Papa picked.

Traditions

Indian Woman
Frederick Niven

The end of it all was that in the spring of 1858 young Angus Munro (just nineteen then) took his woman — it was never *my wife: my woman* it was — to the factor, her father and mother with them, to have an entry made of his union with Minota Red Shield in the company's books.

He did not ask himself insistently why that was all, why he did not go to the mission and have a white man's marriage. He silenced the inquiry by telling himself that some white men took their woman to wife without even the formality of an entry in the books, no more formality than the present of a gun or a few horses to the father.

What was the depth of his love? What was the depth of hers? Her eyes had clouded when, her promise to be his woman given, he had said that they had better have it written down at the Fort; but she had not asked, instead, for a prayer-book ceremony. Minota would have gone with him even without that. He offered neither gun nor horse to old Red Shield. She did not want that; her father, she said, did not want that. That savage, Chief Red Shield, and his woman looked upon it as an honour to have their daughter wed to a white man. Minota's mother was a sonsy woman, coming to the age when those of her race have a tendency to broaden in a very definite "middle-age spread", a sonsy woman with genial eyes and a happy laugh. She was a Stony (which is to say an Assiniboine of the west, a Rocky Mountain Assiniboine) whom Red Shield had met once at the House when both her tribe and his were camped close by there to trade.

No — no gun, no horse for the girl but, not as the purchase price, merely as a gift — as the phrases went, *a prairie gift, a gift cut off, a gift in itself,* meaning not given in hope of any return or exchange — he presented Chief Red Shield (on the sober advice of Captain Buchanan) with a silk hat, a second-hand top hat, with a second-hand ostrich feather round it, for the trade-room at Rocky Mountain House had a queer miscellaneous stock of goods.

Within the palisades were two or three cabins from an earlier period, uninhabited, and in one of these, new-caulked in chinks between the logs, with a Franklin stove from the traderoom, Angus took up house with Minota, making the third at that time in the Fort with an Indian woman. He had moved, as it were, another step away from Loch Brendan. This log cabin was not like those at Red River, thatched, but had a roof of split cedar — *cedar shakes.*

Speedily his Cree talk improved. He discovered that there was not only pidgin-English but pidgin-Cree, and that many white people who imagined that they spoke Cree spoke only that. Minota unfolded for him the tenses of the verbs, and he learnt how pliant were the sentence formations, how full the vocabulary, and that often with one word could be conveyed what necessitated the use of half a dozen English to express. He came to respect *les sauvages* more and more.

As she taught him her language his mind often went back to Sabbath evenings in Scotland, Sabbath evenings at Red River, and the voice of his father (or of Fraser) would be with him again, reading in the Scriptures. For to the same simple, elemental, eternal things did the Crees go for imagery as the Hebrews. *The winter is past, the rain is over and gone, the flowers appear on the earth, the time of the singing birds is come and the voice of the turtle is heard in the land,* might have been one of Minota's songs. *Like as a hen gathering her chickens under her wings* was pure Cree, it struck him. When she taught him the sign language even more did he recall the voice of his father rolling out the Hebraic metaphor in the candlelight at Brendan. If one would signify in the sign language *I am happy,* so Minota showed him, one made the signs for *day* and *my heart,* meaning: *The day is in my heart.* There seemed to be no giving of orders in the talk of the hands. There was no *Do that,* no *Do not do that.* Instead there was *I think it good for you to do that,* or *I think it not good to do that.*

The names of the months, the moons, she told him, beginning with the moon before winter; the moon when the leaves fall; the moon when deer rut; the moon when deer shed their horns; the moon that is hard to bear; the moon when the buffalo cow's foetus is large; the moon of sore eyes (because of the sunlit snow then); the moon when the geese lay eggs; the moon of growing grass; the moon when strawberries ripen; the moon when the buffalo bulls are fat; the moon when the buffalo cows are in season; the moon of red plums. She showed him games, gambling games with little pegs, peeled wands; and one that was simply cup-and-ball Indian fashion.

Well though she could speak English she could read neither print nor script, nor did she know the Cree syllabics devised at Norway House by the Methodist missionary there, James Evans, for her people. Pictograph she could have translated, with the symbolic colourings among the figures represented, but not these symbols. The Woods Crees speedily learnt them but the Plains Crees, roving about in bands, buffalo hunters chiefly, had not the same need to leave missives behind as those who split up into small parties and families for their hunting and trapping in the Land of Little Sticks. The day was to come when Angus would regret that he had not taught her to write.

Like most white men he had looked upon *savages* as signifying something ceaselessly vindictive and treacherous. Red River had corrected that. Like most white men he had looked upon the religion of his people as the only true faith and discarded that view while living with Minota. Very tenderly he came to think of her as she lost her shyness before him and revealed what lived behind these dark, deerlike eyes, behind that soft-moving and graceful exterior. She reminded him at times, by reason of her innocence, her naïveté, of his mother, and occasionally, with her heresies, of his father. She could not understand, for example, simple though it is to the civilized mind, how the company that sold firearms to the Crees was the same that sold firearms to the Blackfeet, Blackfeet and Cree being hereditary enemies. The shareholders in armament firms that gaily, in our days, manufacture lethal weapons for any who will buy she could not have understood.

There were moments when, in place of feeling that he had condescended, or descended, in this alliance, he felt that he was in the presence of something far superior. She was credulous, pathetically so, he thought often, but that credulity, he realized, was from her honesty and truthfulness. She told him of the Blackrobe that came to the Piegans southward with what was called the seventh day ceremonials.

"And one day," said she, "a Piegan went out to hunt, and the Blackrobe saw him going and called to him that it was the Rest Day. The Indian laughed at him and" — her eyes were solemn as she continued, "he was killed that day by a grizzly bear. So the Blackrobe stood up before all the people and told them that God has sent the bear to punish that man, and the next time he rang his bell and called that it was the Day of Rest he had a great gathering in his lodge for the ceremonial. Do you think," she ended, "that God would send a grizzly to kill the man for not resting on His Day?"

Angus shook his head slowly, saying nothing.

"After that Blackrobe left them he went through the

Flathead country and there he baptized a great many, all under the water in a river. And after he had baptized them they went on a war party against the Crows and got many horses, without any being killed. The Blackfeet heard of it and waited for him to come back and got him to baptize a lot of them, and then they went out horse-stealing into the Gros Ventre country, and it was the most successful raid they had had for many snows."

She looked into his eyes.

"You think there is nothing in it?" she asked, trying to read his thoughts.

He was in a quandary similar to that of parents who have had formal religious upbringing and wonder, grown to years of questioning, whether they should bring their children up to a belief in all the old stories or not. She pressed the point.

"You think there is nothing in it?" she repeated.

"I do not know," he said.

It was clear to her he would not say any more than that.

Of her own people's medicine-men she had been rendered somewhat skeptical. They demanded much when they came to shake their rattles, beat their drums, blow their whistles and sing over sick people. She thought that many men and women could do more for illness with herbs and certain roots made into plaisters. Not but what she herself knew of a medicine-man who did a wonderful thing. He cut with a flint a crack in the side of an ailing woman, sucked some of the bad blood there, spat in forth, and lo, he had sucked a little frog from her inside.

"Did she recover?" Angus asked.

"Yes, she recovered at once, and her man gave the medicine-man ten ponics, for he was very fond of her."

She told him the medicine-men were paid chiefly with ponies and buffalo robes. But when anyone was dead their powers ended. The good Father Lacombe at Fort Edmonton had power even after men died. That beautiful black horse he rode he had received from a widow for getting the soul of her dead husband out of purgatory.

"All round us is mystery," said Minota.

Angus nodded slowly, listening.

"Yes," he replied.

"We have the same belief," she said.

There came to Rocky Mountain House news of the Sepoy Mutiny. What was it all about? they wondered. The first emotion was, no doubt, that whatever its cause, enemies of Britain, and rebels, must take their punishment. But soon there was sympathy at the Fort with the mutineers when they heard more. Living among a people prone to superstitions and respecting these if for no other reason than that the amenities might continue and Trade go well, the general view was British arrogance had made a mess among the Sepoys. Angus, after hearing the talk, explained to Minota thus: Much as in the way that the Crees will eat dog, a dish that is abhorrent to the Blackfeet, it was *bad medicine* to some of the people away off there to touch pig and to others the cow was sacred. A new sort of rifle was issued to these people, the cartridges of which needed to be greased, and they had found out that the grease used was that of pig and cow. They objected, and their objection was unheeded — hence the Indian Mutiny.

"Could they not have let the beaver fat, or some other fat, be used?" asked Minota. "That would have put the matter well."

"They would never think of that," replied Angus, deep in him a hatred of tyranny, of the arrogant.

He would talk to her of his early home on Loch Brendan, of how his people had been driven first from fruitful soil to barren soil by the salt-water edge, and then harried even from that. Her eyes had fear in them.

"There are some of my people," said she, "who think that the day will come when we will be treated that way by yours, but I cannot think so. I think there are many more good than bad white people, enough good to keep the bad from doing that to us. I think if they tried to my people would die fighting. Did your people fight?"

"Not where I was. Our medicine-men said we were to go and that if we offered resistance we would sizzle in hell."

"You do not believe in hell fire?"

"I — do — not!" he replied.

The year slipped past. There came the moon when the deer shed their horns, December, and preparations were made for Christmas Day (Big Sunday) with Oregon grape branches in place of holly. The doings of Big Sunday somewhat puzzled the innocence and directness of Angus's woman. According to an old usage of his Highland home he set a lit candle in the window on Christmas eve, and hearing the significance of that — a light for the dead to see — Minota took it much more seriously than he. All night she was hushed, thinking of, as she called them, *the shadows* seeing that signal — his father, his mother, his brother who had been drowned in the big water. Angus had difficulty in explaining to her that he was not sure if the shadows would really see. She thought they would — and they left it at that.

At the Fort the Nativity was celebrated in the usual way. *Braw claes* were worn as they had been worn on high-days and days of celebration all across that land, from the Great Lakes and from Hudson Bay to the Pacific from the beginnings of the fur trade. A prospector from the mountains (there were many such in the land, much gold having been found the year before far west in the Cariboo Country, by white men who had wandered all that way from California) drank so much rum that he died of alcoholic poisoning next day. Minota was troubled over that.

"Did they get drunk," she asked, "at the last feast before He was nailed up on the cross?"

"I should hardly think so."

"My father once got drunk and spewed in the lodge and was very much ashamed. I think Jesus Christ would not like His friends to get drunk and be sick on their last feast together. It was a cruel way to kill Him," she added. "That is a sad story."

The new year came and the new year slipped along. The

moon of the sore eyes was none too bad because of a warm wind (the Chinook) which wiped the snow away. The moon when the geese lay eggs came, geese and ducks honking over, driving their wedges into the north; and Minota sang:

The ice has broken in the rivers,
The geese and the ducks fly over,
All day — and even at night,

But with the spring she grew restless. Her people were moving out of their winter camps, setting up sweat lodges by the river sides and taking baths both wet and dry, as she explained — that is to say steaming themselves in the low brush cages (the sweat lodges), with hot stones thrust into them, and then either cooling outside wrapped in blankets (a dry bath) or plunging into the river afterwards (a wet bath).

The desire to move was agony to Minota. One morning she asked Angus if he would object if she went on a visit to her people who were going from the woods to the plains soon.

"Why, no," said he.

She was troubled lest he should think she loved them more than she loved him, but after more parley and mutual assurances of devotion, and assurance of understanding from him, she took off her white woman's clothes, attired herself in the deerskin kirtle and leggings, wrapped herself in a blanket, and prepared to go. On the point of departure she almost remained. Her people, said she, would come into the Fort some day, and she could see them then. So it was his part to beg her to go and tell her he knew how she felt. As he spoke she looked long in his eyes, loving and troubled.

After she had gone, Tom Renwick chaffed him about his woman.

"Well, your woman has gone back to the blanket!" he said.

Angus felt he had either to take that remark as friendly jest, or to fell him. He wished that Tom's smile had been pleasanter as he spoke, to make the acceptance of his speech as a joke more easy.

"That's it," he answered, "that's it," and lightly laughed as one does when humouring another with whom for this or that reason he has to associate and would bide with amicably, though at heart he would fain see far.

Minota came back within a month, after many sweat-baths, smelling of sweet-grass which she carried in a little sack hanging from a thin raw-hide string round her neck.

In the moon when the strawberries ripen there was a suggestion by Buchanan that they might soon have finished all their work there and have to go to Fort Edmonton; and then arrived at Rocky Mountain House — Sam Douglas. He had been far beyond Edmonton into the mountains by the Howse Pass and Tête Jaune Cache Pass. He had made thorough survey of the foothill country between the ranges and Edmonton, wintering (for his first year) with Macaulay at Jasper House and (for his second) with Colin Fraser at St. Ann's. He was well content. There was coal "almost anywhere", said he. He was going back to *the Old Country* to "interest capital", and had come to Rocky Mountain House because he had been told there might be those there who could convoy him to Fort Brenton on the Missouri River.

No! Impossible! Attempts had been made to open a transport route that way — and failed. The Blackfeet to the south contested the passage of all. Even in mid-summer when they would be out on the plains none could risk that traverse. Angus could see, at that, that Douglas was perturbed. He evidently had no desire to cross the thousand miles to Fort Garry alone. The Crees were friendly, but there was always the risk of coming on some Blackfoot raiding party in their country. He smoothed a hand over his head, meditating. Angus laughed, surmising Douglas's cogitations.

"Yes," said he, "you have a fine, fair scalp-lock trophy there to deck the lodge of a Blackfoot on the South Saskatchewan!"

"That's just the trouble," said Sam, "that and the

loneliness. I am not a man that can live alone. I've been alone enough of late, since last we parted. I was alone in the mountains till I heard voices there. Oh, man, man, I have heard the water-kelpies — and no use to assure me it was but a boulder rumbling down in the spate, or the freshets, as some of them say here, or the rise and fall of a wind that made the creeks cry loud and then hush. No, I canna thole the loneliness."

"When the voices of the dead are heard," explained Minota, "those who have been to the Catholic Mission make this sign," and she showed him. "The Methodist ones just pray without a sign. We pray and make the sign of *I pity you* to them, like this — or like this, *I bless you."*

The grace of her motions held Douglas's eye with admiration, and then —

"Aye," said he. "Well, I think I would make all the signs."

She agreed to that suggestion.

"The more signs the better," said she.

"Would you," began Sam, turning again to Angus, "think of accompanying me across the plains? In fact, I was wondering if you would come all the way with me, seeing the boat-building is nearly finished. Since seeing the coal fires here I have been thinking that evidence of a person living here would be of great help. They might look upon me as a mere promoter, ye ken, but if I had one of the men of the land wi' me . . . "

There came to Angus what, in Minota's absence with her people that spring, had often come to him. He saw, he heard, he smelt the old land. Often, while she had been away, he had looked at the Rockies to the west and seen a peak there like Ben Chattan that stands over the head of Loch Brendan. The forest along the slopes he had, by half shutting his eyes, turned into heather and moors. At Douglas's suggestion he saw, in memory, the seaweed fringe of Scotland undulating to the tides that pound in from the Atlantic, in his reverie saw the silver reflection of the weaving gulls in the dark waters of the loch. The wood smoke and coal smoke odours of the Mountain

House were changed to the smell of smouldering peat.

"I would pay all expenses," said Douglas. We could even arrange something in the manner of a stipend. You have conned your book" — (it was his father's phrase too) — "and you could be of great service secretarially, too, I have nae doot." He always broadened his speech when he was engaged upon a special pleading.

Angus turned to his woman.

"Minota," said he. "It is as you felt in the spring when you had to go and see your people."

"I know it," she replied.

"If I went, what would you do till I came back?" he asked her.

She did not answer at once and Sam, with a manner as of stealth, clearing his throat, stepped to the door, looked out, the girl's dark eyes gazing after him — reproachfully, it seemed.

"I could arrange for you to have everything here you would want while I was away," said Angus.

She shook her head.

"No, It would be easier with my people. Here . . ." she hesitated.

Douglas went strolling out, his hands clasped behind his back.

"No, I would go to my people until," she looked at Angus with doubt in her eyes, he thought, "you come back."

Angus wondered if among her people would be some, like Tom Renwick, who would jest at her that her white man would never return. That look of doubt on her face hurt him. He had an inspiration how to wipe it away. On the impulse he withdrew the collet-ring of his forebears and, taking her hand in his, put it on her third finger. He had compromised between a Blackrobe ceremony and the less ritualisic Indian ceremony of marriage — which was none at all, unless the delivery of a string of horses at the father's door be called ceremony. He had only had the union entered in the Company's books. If she had desired more, now did he abruptly atone.

She was surely his by the light in her eyes then. Had he never before realized how deep was her devotion — her fealty — he knew it at that moment. "I will wait for you," she said, "til you come back from the country of your people. I will wait for you — with my people."

Region and Heritage
Maara Haas

Last night, setting the table for Ukrainian Christmas Eve supper, I thought to myself: "The crazy world is getting crazier and crazier; everything around me is changing so fast I can't grasp it, and here I am, going through the same old ritual, imitating my mother as I remember her when I was five years old, and my grandmother before her. And I bring out my cross-stitch tablecloth, yellow with age; my mother's cutglass bowl for the holy wheat; my grandmother's blue bowl, a cherished reminder of Krakow, Poland, traditionally used for the apricot, prune, and pear compote."

Region, place, environment — these are things you can escape if you try hard enough.

Escape your heritage?

Never. It goes where you go; it sleeps where you sleep. No matter how often you wash your hands, it's there — ingrained in every pore of your body and spirit.

in
dian
Skyros Bruce

we are north americans
he said
and made me feel
ashamed that i was not wearing
beads at my throat
small proud flowers
growing there
or leather
sarain stump
handsome faced
color of earth rose
quietly
telling me that i am
indian now
and ending all
the identity fears
the spiritual smell
of burning sweet grass
i smoke from the pipe
my brother passed to me
i pass it to my sister
it goes around

Early Emigrant
Delphine Burrell

This thinking to return, this going back —
All very well, and needful, now I know.
How can a long displaced and yearning heart
Renew its allegiance, but to go?
How strong the pull of distant birthland shore.
How loud the call of loved ones far away.
How swift the passing of a lifetime's years.
Yet strange the thought that still — you just
    may stay.

For what of all the lives you've intertwined
With yours, in passing of each goodly year?
Unconsciously the sturdy roots you've grown
In this, your own adopted country here.
So now, I have a fear the time will come
When of your heart you'll ask, "Which one is
    home?"

A Visit to the Immigrant Sheds
Laura Goodman Salverson

Another time, we went to the immigrant sheds to meet some
Icelanders who were arriving from "home", and had neither
relatives nor friends in this country. It was not unusual for such
people to write to my father, for he was known through his
writings in the Icelandic periodicals, and he seemed to take it
for granted that he should help these strangers through the
ordeal of endless questionings, medical inspection, customs
ritual, and, finally steer them to some sort of temporary
quarters.

It was Sunday, on this occasion. In one respect, this was a happy circumstance, for it meant no loss of time from his work at the saddlery, where he eked out a meagre living under the time-honoured piecework system beloved of all sweatshop autocrats. On the other hand, it meant precious hours away from his hobby, from the one thing that kept him alive — his cherished writing.

"Six days, I may be a slave," papa used to say. "On Sunday, I am my own man, and live to please myself."

It was quite a ritual. Breakfast coffee over, he shined his shoes, washed, put on his white shirt, dark trousers, and a rusty old Prince Albert, and when he was sure not a hair was out of place, his moustache neatly trimmed and his tie perfectly straight, he pocketed his silver snuff-box, and, cane in hand, set out for a little walk. Sometimes he went to church — preferably to the Ukrainian Meeting House, where ideas, not emotions, were exploited. Sometimes he called on his sick friend. But, invariably, when he came back, and dinner was over and done, he retired to his barren room to write for the rest of the day, perfectly contented, and unconscious of what went on in the rest of the house.

Now, however, he had to visit the immigrant sheds. It was a warm summer's day, with not a cloud in the sky, or a murmur of wind. The air would do me good, he told mamma, a little defiantly. That was another bone of contention between them. Papa maintained I should run about more freely, but my poor mother, always terrified that I might go the way of her other babies, would have wrapped me in mothballs and locked me in a glass case if she could. This time, the perfect weather and a patchwork quilt she was eager to finish spoke in our favour. So there I was, dressed in a clean pinafore, with ruffles on the shoulders that stood out like wings, and my pigtails neat, yellow ropes bobbing from under a little straw hat, walking sedately beside papa, who had faithfully promised to keep a slow pace, so that I should not get a fit of coughing from breathlessness.

There was really no danger of excessive haste. Papa knew his own weakness, and had set off in ample time. A few houses down the street a stout woman was picking marigolds in her patch of garden. She was puffing and blowing, and red as a beet, and her mouse-coloured hair straggled down from a hard knot at the back of her neck. Papa stopped, leaning on his cane.

"How fine you look, Marta," said he, with a hint of flattering surprise. "My, my, what flowers! It is easy to see you have the touch a lovely garden needs."

Marta stifled a gasp, as she straightened her cricked back, mopping a wet brow, and smiled at papa.

"I'm not so bad, thank God," said she. "But those devils of cutworms come up in droves after the rain — and that was quite a shower we had last night. Three or four o'clock it was, I know, for I hadn't shut an eye, what with my bad leg, and Benjamin a snorer."

"Those are beautiful flowers," papa interrupted an impending deluge, pointing to a bed of sweet-william and verbena.

"Brightish, kind of," Marta agreed. "If I didn't see you are visiting-bent, I'd give you some, and welcome — maybe the little one would like a posy any way."

"You heart is as good as your garden, Marta," papa rejoined. "I'd be glad of a few flowers, if you can spare them. We are off to the immigrant sheds — you know how it is for the stranger."

"What a thoughtful soul you are!" exclaimed Marta, and set to work selecting her choicest flowers for a fragant offering. With these in my arms, we continued our leisurely way.

Safely out of earshot, I said: "Papa, did you really want these — for the strangers?"

"Perhaps not, Lala," papa smiled at me. "Perhaps I wanted the old woman to be happy. It makes people happy, to share beautiful things."

Our next stop was a corner store, where papa bought a little round carton of snuff, and a red apple for me. . . . At last we neared the confluence of the Red and Assiniboine Rivers, and saw, down on the bank, the long, low structure that was the immigrant shed. I don't remember much about it, except that it was a grimy, forbidding place, with dirty windows and battered doors. We stepped out of the brilliant prairie sunshine into a grey gloom, and exchanged the sweet summer air for a stale, indescribable smell, which haunts me to this day. It was a sickening compound of rancid oils and animal odours that seemed to be carried on every faintest current of breeze from the room which gave off the small information office wherein we stood.

Papa coughed, took out his snuff-box, hastily inhaled a pinch of the pungent powder, coughed again, and hurried to the information desk. Yes, the Icelanders had arrived, the clerk informed him. They were waiting in the second doorway whence the evil smells drifted.

"Go ahead," the man told him. "Just a bunch of Doukhobors in there. There's nothing to stop you."

No, there was nothing to stop us, except a hundred human forms stretched out upon the dirty floor, close-packed as locusts in a year of plague. Strange, human bundles, which, to my terrified glance, seemed more like animals, than men, for they were all wrapped in greyish, woolly, skin garments, that reeked with horrible odour. That they were human beings I realized, however, as we picked our way, stepping over a sprawling leg or outflung arm or an entire inert form. Sometimes, a heavy head would lift from its sheepskin collar, and eyes like coals stare at us out of a thicket of matted hair and beard. Sometimes, a beardless face turned on us, vacantly, blinked empty eyes, and dropped back to the comfort of a sheepskin sleeve, or the hill of a smaller bundle, which may have been a child, or a tightly rolled feather tick.

To my excited fancy, they seemed a race of hairy monsters, stewing in their own reek, like the animals in a circus. I could not skip through them fast enough. That is how I came to trip, sprawling on a huge fellow who lay spilled out in peace just inside the door I was so eager to reach. Of course, I lost my Marta's gift of flowers, and if I didn't scream it was because the fright was shocked out of me when the huge bolster jacked-up like a spring, and the big, bearded face stared at me, crinkled with smiles. What was more, the surprising creature retrieved the bouquet of flowers, which had fallen behind him. Before he could hand them back, however, as was his evident intention, a woman beside him snatched them from his hand, and buried her hot, grimy face in their sweet petals.

"Come, child," papa's voice called me.

"But, papa, my flowers — "

Then I saw that papa was smiling in a queer way at the woman, who seemed to be seeing nothing but the little bunch of flowers from a prairie garden.

"Come, my dear," he repeated, softly.

On Being Canadian
Michael Luchkovich

Sir: — *The Journal's* recent editorial of April 6, 1962, "Discourage Hyphenated Canadianism", would have been more convincing had it been intended to apply from the top down instead of from the bottom up. Are you not aware the British Isles are the most highly integrated country in the world with their English, Scots, Welsh and Irish ethnic groups, and that it is the successful application of this principle that has made those islands the wonder of the world? For integration has strengthened rather than weakened Great Britain. The same can be said of Switzerland, another marvel in the realm of genuine integration with its triple national set-up.

If "Hyphenated Canadianism" were as odious as was indicated in your article, then why were so many questions being asked during the recent taking of the census concerning the ethnic origin of each citizen? Records are being kept of the number of each one of these ethnic units in Canada, and subsequent research will be made by scholars into these statistics, so whether we like it or not, each one of them is classified as a German, Ukrainian, Swedish, Polish or otherwise hyphenated Canadian. Thus the more we try to slough off the principle of "Hyphenated Canadianism", the more stubbornly it keeps coming back to us, not as a bugbear, but as a natural process in the complexity of Canadianism.

Although much has been made of the "melting pot", I do not like its stifling fumes. I fail to see any evidence of its alleged success. Do you for one moment imagine that the process of Canadianization is as simple as throwing all our prospective citizens into one cauldron and then expecting a finished product to be molded in conformity with our preconceived ideas of what such citizens should be? "Finished" is right, but not in the way our reformers contemplated. The melting pot is merely a method to reduce the citizen to conformity, a procrustean way of whittling him down to preconceived size, instead of allowing him to develop naturally along the lines of his own nature, ability and inclination.

A few months ago, I heard a Scotsman dressed in kilts, with bagpipes over his shoulder, sing the praises of his race and eulogize Robbie Burns as the greatest poet. Well, that was all right with me. I honored him for his display of self-respect. But do not other ethnic groups also wish to walk with dignity? Of course they do; but that does not make them less Canadian. Indeed, such widely different personages as the Right Honourable John Diefenbaker, Hon. Paul Martin, and Lord Tweedsmuir have all united in conformity to the doctrine that you will become a "better Canadian by being a better

Ukrainian". Being loyal to one's ethnic extraction does not mean disloyalty to Canada; on the contrary, as in Great Britain, it enhances it.

As regards our children, they will settle their own affairs, far better by themselves than would be the case by any intrusion or pressure from above. In this regard, a glance at the social columns in *The Journal* should be a revelation to its readers.

Heritage
Magda Rice

From childhood's dappled years I glean
Norwegian stories told beside
our warm Canadian fires.
On frost encrusted nights we heard
of other childhoods in another land.
Our mother told of twilight days
and summers circling sun
moonlight on the birches
pines of Finmark, Alta by the sea.
With far off gaze she told
of Norway's fiords like ours
and fishing fleets at Hammerfest
and Solvejg's song.
They sang their hymns of praise
around their Christmas tree
as we were circling ours,
their Silent Night
their Holy Night was ours.
We knew her northern lights
from those that ringed our skies
like guardian fires in our Canadian nights.

My Home, My Home
I-Syin

Home was Hong Kong, with grandpa,
    grandma and many little cousins,
Hot crowded streets with toy stands
    and food stalls and steaming hot buns,
Hovering over them giant skyscapers
Beaches full of happy faces and sun-burnt
    children, splashing in the water;
A ride in the train and once even in a
    rickshaw, and a car ferry across the
    harbour.

        Canada is new, different, spacious and
            Oh, very cold
        Calgary is nice, with snow capped
            mountains and beautiful Banff.
        Calgary is 'Hi' from a friendly neighbour,
        The Stampede under the hot sun,
            sticky candy floss all over your face,
        The excitement of the rodeo and
            chuckwagon races.

Calgary is being bundled up in heavy
    clothing, with frosted nose and face,
Skating with friends in winter frolics.
Calgary is having new pets, yelping and
    romping in the large backyard.
Calgary is now home, and a happy one too.

British Columbia Gothic

Marya Fiamengo

In the Kootenay country
at Nelson
where cold water
gives asylum to hot hills
an Ukrainian woman
serves me coffee.

I look into her
water pale blue eyes
bleached by time
weather dim like my mother's
sea-stained Adriatic eyes
and I hear Mayokovsky shout,

"Mother the Germans have murdered
evening in the street."

And it does not comfort
nor amuse me
to read in the Nelson Daily News
of July 13th
that the mountain town of Kimberley
has gone Bavarian
for the summer tourist trade.

Berchtesgaden in the British Columbia hills
the kitch of lederhosen
adding foreign colour
to local commercial flair

I wonder
where are the Doukhobors
and the Jews?

Where Is My Home?

Lark Song

W. Kinsella

If we'd of been smart we never would have let Joseph go off by himself that Saturday in Wetaskiwin. But we did, and there sure been a lot of trouble for everybody ever since. My brother, Joseph Ermineskin, be older than me. He is 22 already, but when he just a baby he catch the scarlet fever and his mind it never grow up like his body do.

Joseph ain't crazy. He just got a tiny kid's mind in a big man's body. He is close to six feet tall and broad across the shoulder. His face is round and the colour of varnished wood. He be gentle and never hurt nobody in his whole life.

Unless you look right in his eyes he don't look no different than the rest of us guys. We let his hair grow long, and we got him a denim outfit, and once when I worked at a mine for the summer, I bought him a pair of cowboy boots. But Joseph he smile too often and too long at a time. I guess it because his mind ain't full of worries like everybody else.

Joseph ain't no more trouble to look after than any other little kid and he is even good at a couple of things. He can hear a song on the radio and then play it back on my old guitar just like he heard it. He forget it pretty quick though, and can usually only do it one time.

And he can sound like birds. He caws like the crows so good that they come to see where the crow is that's talking to them. He talk like a magpie too, but best of all he sound like a meadowlark. Meadowlarks make the prettiest sound of any bird I ever heard, when they sing it sound like sweet water come bubble up out of a spring.

Sometime when we sit around the cabin at night and everyone is sad, Joseph he make that lark song for us and soon everyone is feel some better because it so pretty.

It is funny that he can do that sound so good, cause when he talk he sound like the wind-up record player when it not cranked up good enough. His voice is all slow and funny and he have to stop a long time between words.

One time, Papa, when he still lived here with us, is take Joseph with him to Wetaskiwin. Papa he get drunk and don't come home for a week or so, but the very next day, Joseph he is show up. He is hungry and tired from walk all those miles down the highway, but he find his way home real good. He is smile clear around to the back of his neck when he see us, and he don't ask about go to town with anybody for a long time after that.

Still I can tell he feel bad when me and my friend Frank Fence-post and all the guys go into town in Louis Coyote's pickup truck and leave him at home. That was why we take him one Saturday afternoon with us. We put him in the park to play while we go look in the stores and maybe stop for a beer or two. Joseph sure like the swings, and being strong and tall he can sure swing up high. What we should of told him though, and didn't, was for sure not to play with none of them white kids.

White people don't like nobody else to touch their kids, especially Indians. Here on the reserve it's kind of like one family, the kids run free when they is little and nobody minds if somebody else hugs your little boy or girl.

Joseph he like little kids and they like him back. Big people don't always have time, or maybe they don't want to, love their kids as much as they should. Joseph is pick up the kids when they fall down, or maybe when they is just lonesome. He don't say nothing to them, just pet their heads like maybe they was little kittens, hold them close and make them feel warm. Sometimes he make his bird sounds for them, and they forget why they feel bad, hug his neck, and feel good that someone likes them.

People say that was what happen in the park in Wetaskiwin that day. A little girl is fall off the slide and hurt herself. When Joseph see her crying he is just pick her up like he would an Indian kid. Only them kids all been told, don't mess around with strangers, and somebody runs for some mothers.

We come back to get Joseph about the same time that little girl's mother come to get her. If you ever seen a lady partridge fly around on the ground pretend she got a broken wing so her enemy go after her and leave her young ones alone, that is how that white lady is act.

Joseph is just stand in the sandbox hold that little girl in his arms, and she is not even crying anymore until she hear her mother scream and dance up and down. I sure afraid for what might have happen to Joseph if we don't come when we did.

I unwrap his arms from the little girl and hand her back to the lady, who is cry some and yell a lot of bad things at us and say somebody already called the RCMP.

The RCMP guys come roll up in their car with the lights flash and I sure wish we was all someplace else. While everyone try to yell louder than everyone else, Joseph he sit down and play some in the sand and every once in a while he make his meadowlark call.

I try to explain to them RCMP guys that Joseph he is about as harmless as that meadowlark he is sounding like. Meadowlarks ain't very pretty or good for much but make beautiful sounds, but they sure don't hurt nobody either, I tell them.

Lots of people is standing around watching and I think they figure something real bad has happened. There is a real big white lady with a square face is carry a shotgun.

We promise the RCMP guys and anybody else that will listen that for sure we never gonna bring Joseph to town no more. We keep him on the reserve forever and then some, we tell them.

For once it look like maybe the RCMP is gonna believe us Indians. They say they can't see no reason to lay any charges, cause all it look like Joseph done was to pick up a kid that fall down. The white girl's mother is yell loud on everybody, say if the RCMP ain't gonna do nothing she'll go to somebody who will. And that lady with the square face wave her shotgun and say she would sure like to shoot herself a few wagon-burners.

After we all go to the police station for a while the RCMP let us take Joseph home, but it is only a couple of days until some Government people is come nose around our place a lot. They is kind of like the coyotes come pick at the garbage, we hardly ever see them but we still know they is there.

Two little women in brown suits come to our cabin, say wouldn't we think Joseph be happier in a home someplace where there are lots of other retarded guys.

Ma, like she always do, pretend she don't understand English, and just sit and look at them with a stone face. But she sure is worried.

Next time they come back, they ain't nearly so nice. They say either we put Joseph in the place for crazy people at Ponoka, or they get a judge to tell us we have to.

The next week, me and my girlfriend Sadie One-wound, hitch-hike the twelve miles down to Ponoka to have a look at the crazy place. I know all my life that the place is there but there is something about a place like that that scares us a lot. It makes us too shy to go up to the gate and ask to look around. Instead we just walk around outside for a while. It got big high wire fences but inside there is lots of grass and beds of pretty flowers, and the people who walk around inside don't look as though they trying to run away or nothing.

The Government peoples keep sending Ma big fat letters with red writing on them. One say that Ma and Joseph got to appear at something called a committal hearing at the court room in Wetaskiwin. We figure that if we go there they gonna take Joseph away from us for sure.

I go down to the pay phone at Hobbema Crossing and phone all the way to Calgary to the office of Mr. William Wuttunnee, the Indian lawyer, but he is away on holiday, and no, I say, I don't want nobody to call me or nothing.

We don't go to that committal hearing cause Ma, she say that we just pretend that nothing is happening, and if we do that long enough the white people stop bothering us.

A couple of weeks later we get another big bunch of papers with red seals all over them, delivered by the RCMP guys personal. Them papers say they gonna come and get Joseph on a certain date. We figure it out on the calendar from the Texaco Service Station, and we decide that when they come they ain't gonna find no Joseph. We just put him to live with someone back in the bush a few miles and move him around whenever we have to.

One good thing about white people is that they usually give up easy. The RCMP is always nose around for Sam Standing-at-the-door's still, or maybe have a warrant for arrest somebody for steal car parts or something, but we tear up the culvert in the road from Hobbema to our cabins, and them guys sure hate to walk much, so they just go away after they yell at the closest Indians for a while. We figure the Government people like to walk even less than the RCMP so it be pretty easy to fool them.

I don't know if they came a day early or if maybe we forget a day someplace, but their cars is already across the culvert and halfway up the hill before we seen them. And the guy from the crazy place in Ponoka, who wears a white jacket, look like he be a cook in a cafe, say he is a Métis, and he even talk Cree to us, which is real bad, cause then we can't pretend we don't understand what is happening. Usually, people we don't like go away real quick when we pretend we don't understand, especially if we sharpen a knife or play with a gun while we talk about them some in our language.

This Métis guy tell us, look, they ain't gonna hurt Joseph

down there at the mental hospital, and it only be twelve miles away so we can come visit him anytime. He gonna be warm and clean and have lots of food and he get to make friends with other guys like him and maybe even learn to make things with his hands and stuff.

It don't sound so bad after all, if it true what he says. All we had time to do was hide Joseph under the big bed in the cabin, and he been making bird songs all the time he is under there. Ma, she finally call him to come out, and he poke out his head and smile on everybody.

We pack up his clothes in a cardboard box. He sure ain't got much to take with him. Frank Fence-post ask them guys is they got electric light down at the crazy place, and they tell him the hospital is fully equipped. Frank he goes and gets his fancy-shaped electric guitar that he bought at a pawnshop in Calgary. He tell the guys from the hospital they should show Joseph how to plug the guitar into the wall. Then he shove the guitar into Joseph's arms.

The kids is all come out from the cabins and stand around look shy at the ground while I talk to Joseph, like I would my littlest sister, explain he should be good, and how these guys is his friends and all. Joseph he pet the guitar like it alive and smile for everybody and touch his fingers on the shiny paint of the car from Ponoka.

Once they is gone we sure ain't got much to say to each other. Ma and Frank talk a little about how we go visit Joseph on Saturday, sneak him away and hide him out on the reserve. But it different when they got him than when we got him, and I don't think that idea ever gonna come to much.

I don't sleep so good that night. I am up early. The sky is clear and the sun is just come up. There is frost on the brown grasses and the slough at the foot of the hill is frozen thin as if window glass had been laid across it. Brown bulrushes tipped with frost, stand, some straight, some at angles, like spears been stuck in the ground. Outside the cabin door our dogs lie curled like horse collars in their dirt nests. They half open their yellow eyes, look at me then go to sleep again. The air is thin and clear and pine smoke from another cabin is rise straight up like ink lines on paper. From the woodpile I carry up an armful of split pine. The wood is cold on my arm and I tuck the last piece under my chin.

Then there is like an explosion from down the hill and across the slough someplace. Like a gunshot, only beautiful. The crows rise up like they been tossed out of the spruce trees.

At first I want to laugh it sound so funny, the voice of a summer bird on a frosty morning. Then it come again, that sweet, bubbly, blue-sky-coloured lark song. I do laugh then, but for happy, and I toss the wood on the ground and run for the meadow.

Each Mountain
Sid Marty

Each mountain
its own country
in the way a country
must be
A state of mind

News of the mountains
brought out by the horse guides
long time ago, though some old boys
live long, tell it still in legion halls
how they cut trails to the high tundra
packing a few adventurers
through deadfall of the timber bands
last of the taiga
to find their way

bright with wild cranberry
and flowers.

Each mountain
where local climate
controls the shade
of paintbrush and anemone
Colours and moods
vary as the weather, suddenly.

But we belonged here too
men and women
our loving squalls
intemperate desires
wide ranging
hot and cold
like August glaciers
as we travelled for pleasure
walking above the trees
and climbing the summits
Because the smell
of wild mountain flowers
of a thousand hues
threatened the civilized monster
carried in us from the highway.

Must be tempered
with the threat of loss
Thus we gain
romantics because
each mountain
made us so
would not have us
any other way.

Kirby's Gander
John Patrick Gillese

I was grabbing some air outside the Cavu Club when, far above me, I heard the slow clang of geese bucking head winds, winging north. *Ho-woak*-clang! *Oak-woak*-clang! Like wild bugles in the night.

"That's the old gander," a voice said behind me. "Cheering 'em up keeping them going."

I turned and saw a big, broad-shouldered fellow standing in the shadows. I sensed he was the bush flier Mike Farrell had told me about. The one who was marooned at Moon Lake, 300 miles this side of the tundra, for five and a half months.

"You're Kirby? Red Kirby?"

"That's right, kid." The man flipped his cigarette into the dark and looked up at the velvet sky. It tasted like rain. "And some of those guys up there — maybe they know me."

I said nothing. Kirby smiled faintly.

"New, aren't you?"

"Just got my licence. Jim Morrison's my name. I trained under Mike Farrell."

"You'll do, then," Kirby said. "And it's a good life you've chosen, kid. Sometimes, though, you'll get a funny feeling, flying over that bush. There's a million square miles of it. But if you ever have to land, just remember that any man who keeps his head and makes the most of his emergency supplies can survive indefinitely. The one thing you have to worry about is the loneliness. You have the feeling you're the last person alive in creation. That's why guys get crazy notions, like trying to walk out. Don't ever try it, kid. The muskegs, the lakes, the mountains — ugh-ah. Stay put, kid. Get your mind on something else."

Kirby paused. "Normally," he said apologetically, "I don't talk like this. But sometimes on a spring night — when I hear them calling — I like to shake it out of my system. If you're in a hurry to get back in there —"

I said I wasn't; and Kirby proceeded to tell me about his gander.

I was four hours out of Edmonton (Kirby said) headed for Great Bear, when I knew I'd had it. Lost my oil — I never did discover how — and when the engine seized, I got all the speed I could, trying to make a flat plateau lying south of Moon Lake. Couldn't do'er, though, so I did the next best — came in-wind, making for the uphill slope to the east. There was an avenue of scrub poplars there — knocked the wings squarely off the old Norseman and slowed her down beautifully. Didn't even have to chop the door off.

That was on the 27th of April. There was the odd patch of snow left, but around the lake the birch had pink tips. I noticed that because I was hoping they'd find me before the bush got so green and dense you couldn't spot an army in it.

After I got over the tight tension of those first few days (you feel the search parties are up there looking, and you're on edge to make sure they don't just fly close and then pass on, you know), I spent a while exploring the region and, of course, watching the waterfowl coming back. Except for the Canada geese, which have long memories where man is concerned, nothing paid the slightest attention to me. Even the geese were hard put to reconcile my presence in their age-old breeding grounds.

Take the morning I saw the timber wolf. I'd gone down to the inlet to throw a spinner for a trout, and there was this big black bruiser pawing on the shore weeds. He opened his mouth, lolled his tongue like a dog, and bounded toward me. For a minute, all I could think of was the .22 back in the tent. Then he spotted two muskrats slashing the hides off each other farther down the shore, and away he went. He was only curious, you know — I suppose I was the first man he'd ever seen. Crazy devil started following my tracks all over the place after a while, picking up any fish and partridge offal I threw away.

But it was the waterfowl that really intrigued me. At the time I crashed, millions of them darkened the flyways, each flock headed unerringly for the lakes and marshes and rivers of their birth. Moon Lake was black with them — mallards and lesser duck breeds mostly — and at night you couldn't sleep for the din.

A couple of hundred Canadas, though, were the real overlords of the lake; well bred, keeping to themselves; never undignified, like the quarrelsome ducks. I figure all the honkers there were related to one big gander and his mate. Old Abraham, I named him — and mister, that gander was the grand-daddy of all wild geese.

Remember the 22-pound flock leader some fellows shot in Manitoba in '43? Well, he had nothing on Old Abraham. I'll bet that gander had been winging back and forth to Moon Lake for 20 years.

And respected? Say, all the geese on that lake knew him. Whenever any of them passed by, they dipped their beaks in the water, sort of like they were paying homage to the old patriarch. Sort of like they were thanking him for all the times he'd guided them down the flyways to Mexico and brought them safely home again.

As the days went by, of course, the waterfowl got over the excitement of homecoming and set about the business of nesting. Then it was mostly drakes you saw, or Canadas that had lost their mates. Did you know if one honker dies or is killed, the other one never mates again?

One morning, when I was fishing a cove on the north of the lake, I suddenly spotted Old Abraham's mate pulling dry grasses for the nest. An abandoned beaver works broke the spring winds that swept across the waters, and from the ridge a nice suntrap sloped down to the reeds. The actual nesting site was about three feet from the water's edge — a hummock of withered goose grass.

Fifty feet out, Old Abraham tacked casually about — those bright eyes weighing every move I made. I slipped quietly away — didn't want to molest them at this stage. Every day after that though, I crept back to watch them.

The routine of the geese never varied. Old Abraham reminded me of a battleship, cruising back and forth, always the same distance from the water line. His mate never left the nest, except for a half hour every afternoon when she unkinked and fed. If a mink or some other prowler got too close to that she-goose, she gave one quack — one long hiss — and the battleship went into action. It was the most fascinating sight I ever watched.

Then one morning, a drizzling black rain confined me to the pup tent. It was the 19th day, and I realized then they weren't going to find me easily — if ever. That's when I started thinking — desperately. About the geese, I mean.

You see, I'd always liked honkers. When I was a kid on the farm, I used to envy them flying over in the fall, then back again in the spring. To me, they were the symbol of everything orderly and free. And I'd read bits about them. Some scientist — Austrian, I think — discovered that the young geese have a fixation complex. First living object they see stirs an emotional attachment in them. Normally, that's the mother. But it might be a cow or a man or even a cat — which is why, even among domestic geese, you'll sometimes see one that's happier following an old horse around than being with its own kind.

The more I thought of it, the more the idea obsessed me. Even if I was stranded there three years, wouldn't it be something to live for, I thought — just to have those geese clanging down out of the sky to me each spring again?

I waited a couple of days more, to be sure old Biddy was really nesting, for if they're still laying, they won't think twice about abandoning one nest and starting another. Then, after another bleak night of rain, I couldn't put it off any longer. I headed for the cove.

The minute I stepped out on that beaver embankment, I'll

swear the geese sensed what was up. Biddy ducked her head into the butter grass and hissed the alarm. Old Abraham came at me, wings out, beak open.

The minute he flapped ashore, I threw my flying jacket over the old boy's head and tackled. That's when I knew his weight and strength. Inside two minutes he'd got one wing free, and I couldn't see for blood. Then I sprawled on the wet reeds, and the old rascal got his neck out. Ever been bitten by a goose?

I got him, though. I finally pinned those big wings under my left arm, and with the big neck stabbing like a snake, I walked over to the nest. His mate flopped off, scattering gray eiderdown over the seven big eggs. I let Old Abraham see me handle them. Then I backed up and let him go.

He jumped right back at me, feathers dishevelled, eyes suffused with blood. Then he gave a hiss and jumped into the water. Out on his patrol line, he threw me one last dirty look and a hiss, then rose on his rudder to straighten his feathers.

It started to drizzle again. Now, I wondered, would old Biddy abandon the nest?

For half an hour, while I huddled on the beaver bank, praying, she sat motionless in the water. With each passing minute, I was getting more scared those eggs would perish.

The same thing must have occurred to Biddy, for she turned slightly and started talking it over with the gander. For fully five minutes more, they exchanged agitated quacks. Then, I presume, the old boy told her to get back on the nest and start incubating. Anyway, she waddled ashore and bent her long neck, to turn the eggs. Then, with her black feet well apart, she stepped up on the hummock and squatted. It was like an omen, the way the shower stopped and the sun broke through.

Even so, I had two more wrestling matches with the old gander before the geese accepted the inevitable. Then, as if it was the most natural thing in the world, they permitted me a daily inspection of the eggs.

The hatching was about four days off — as near as I could

calculate — the morning I looked out of the tent to find a thin mist spiralling up from the lake. Damp weather is depressing when you're in the woods alone, and I was all jumpy, without knowing why. Finally, I grabbed the .22 and headed for the cove.

A hundred yards from the nest, I could hear a fearsome commotion. Soaked to the skin, I pushed through the scrub bush, unable to comprehend what was going on. Feathers and loose hair and old grass were floating in the mist, and occasionally I could see the angry head of the old gander popping above the embankment. The crazy timber wolf and Old Abraham were battling it out.

The wolf was leaping high, trying to snap the thick black neck. Suddenly he changed tactics, closing his teeth on the gander's left wing instead.

Old Abraham quacked in agony. Then he came in on the injured wing, buffeting the wolf with the other. The black devil yowled in his throat, but he wouldn't let go, though the one-winged threshing he was getting sounded like someone pounding a rug with a broom handle.

He began to shake his head madly, trying to rip the wing off; and the gander, hurt though he was, stabbed about the face with his open beak, trying to get the eyes.

I would have shot sooner if I'd had the chance. The wolf turned around, almost stupidly, then staggered to the bushes. He fell on his side, and you should have seen his face. One eye was a bloody pulp. The other was filled with dumb surprise — whether because of the gander or the shot, I don't know.

For Old Abraham, it must have been the toughest fight he'd ever had. Almost exhausted, he stood with his legs apart, his curved neck resting on the grasses. He never protested when I carried him to the water — just lay heavily in my arms, blinking his eyes in pain.

Then I saw a thing I sort of had no right to see. Old Biddy rose off the eggs — the first time I'd seen her voluntarily break her routine — and flopped across to her wounded mate. She quacked softly in her throat, caressing the white patch on his cheeks with her beak.

The gander sat there stolidly — maybe the pain was that unbearable; maybe his pride in his own strength was gone — and that seemed to send her into despair. She talked away, soft and pleading. Maybe telling him about all the pathways they'd flown together — about the good times they'd shared.

Anyway, when I came back that afternoon, they seemed to have found a certain peace again.

I moved the tent and what was left of the emergency supplies — a couple of chocolate bars I'd been saving for the day they found me, fire-tablets, mosquito hood and stuff. I also had a coop I'd made from the aluminum of the plane — hacked it out with the ax and knife, and jabbed plenty of air holes in it. I wasn't taking any chances on those goslings not getting well acquainted with me.

As near as I could reckon, they were hatched on the 12th of June — and by then the days were warm and perfect.

Two of them were already out of the shells when I got up with the sunrise. That part of the day's chilly, though, even in June; and I didn't dare keep old Biddy off the nest just to make sure the others saw the right thing first. Old Abraham hunkered right beside me, his left wing trailing stiffly on the soft new grass, unable to keep away at such a moment.

Every so often, I'd push my hand under old Biddy's feathers — ever been bit by a she-goose? — and pull out a sticky little yellow gosling. It would reel around on the palm of my hand, weaving its chunky little wings for balance. Old Abraham would quack softly to it, Biddy would whisper in her throat, and I'd get in my pleading: "Goo-goo-goosie!" I held it in various position, so it would get a good look at me. I even broke the chocolate bars into small pieces and tried to get them to eat, but they weren't interested. The long-hoarded bars weren't wasted, though — Abe and Biddy picked up the pieces with relish.

After the sixth egg hatched, the she-goose waited for half

an hour, then stuck her head out of sight, listening for life signs in the seventh. At last she got up and rolled it out of the nest; as far as I could determine, it must have got chilled. Then, with the gander marching ahead — proud despite his wing — the mother shepherded the six young into the water. Those little beggars hadn't eaten — they could scarcely stand on their legs — but they swam like veterans. Funny how proud a man could feel, too, about a sight like that.

When it came time to come ashore, I could see the old honkers had plotted this moment beforehand and were trying to pull a fast one on me. They headed for the reeds a hundred yards from the nest.

That moment was about the lowest I'd had since the crash. I can tell you right now I had no faith in science as I stood there, calling softly: "Gee-gee-geese! Come, little goosies — gee-gee-geese!"

Now, I expect my voice had nothing to do with it, except to tell them where I was. At any rate, the Austrian knew his stuff. Four of them came peeping through the reeds to my feet.

Abraham and his mate talked the business over in plainly perplexed tones; then, with the other two young, they waddled, sort of philosophically, towards me. I put them all in a box for the night and weighed the top with a rock. The old geese didn't like it a bit. Abraham gave me the very devil of a nip on the thigh — he was kind of peeved at me for outsmarting them, I think.

It's hard to tell the sex of a gosling, so I named my four: Tiny, Sally, Pedro and Joe. Pretty soon I had a hard time getting away from them, to rustle myself a fish or a grouse. The other two, mind you, accepted me — but the only time my four seemed happy without me was when they were in the water. In a couple of weeks, they were big lumps, their backs turning a definite dark in colour; running madly over the water, little wings flapping, when they were frightened. Each morning they left for the sedges, where the older Canadas tipped in the

shallows or pulled new goose grass, feeding. Each evening —
whether they led the old geese or the old ones brought them,
I was never sure — they swam across to the cove, little wings
spattering the watertop the moment they sighted me. The
smallest one used to squat on my shoe and, after awhile, it
would even sit there while I walked carefully from the shore
to the coop beside my tent.

Pretty soon, I lost all track of time. I knew when it was
mid-summer, for the dews fell heavily; and instead of it getting
dark at night, there was a brief twilight, with pale green skies,
broken with a big orange welt where the sun had gone down.
A dense growth of vines and leaves completely covered the
Norseman, and at night you couldn't sleep for the sticky heat
and the monotonous drone of the mosquitoes. Returning to the
plane one day, I looked at it almost as a caveman might. It was
hard to believe that once it had carried me farther and faster
than even the wild geese fly.

Ten weeks after they were born, my four little geese were
nearly as big as the old ones, and naturally I had to stop putting
them in the coop at night.

I don't suppose I could have raised those goslings to young
adulthood without Old Abraham. At first there were the pike,
lying in wait in the wind riffles. Old Abe knew the toll they take
of young waterfowl; and when the geese swam in dangerous
waters, it was in convoy formation — the gander calling the
warnings, going into action like a depth charge when one of
those raiders streaked upward. Between us, we finished a killer
mink that worried the geese for a week: Abraham beat him up
in the reeds; I shot him when he crawled ashore. And there
were a couple of falcons that used to sit like black stubs on the
trees, striking down the first goose that attempted to fly across
the lake — I got them too. Sometimes Old Abraham would
turn there on the waters, stretching his left wing, as if
acknowledging my help. I hardly felt free to leave the shore for
more than a couple of hours at a time.

One afternoon, as I sat there, feeding, I realized August must be coming to an end. There was a blue haze over the lake and the hills that told me it was the end of summer.

Suddenly from the lake below me came the sound of Old Abraham trumpeting. He knew the signs, too, and he was marshalling the young to try their wings.

I walked across the plateau and looked down on the cloud-blue waters. Young ducks were skip-flighting lightly around the edges of the lake; and in the wide centre, the parent geese were lined up, each family in its own strip, the young between the parents. Abraham and his brood were in the very middle of the waters.

"Oak-woak-honk!" After weeks of muted talking, it was spine-tingling to hear the bugle call again.

The young geese, swimming fast, spread their wings, spattered with their feet — and rose in heavy, wobbly flight into the wind — then, gaining altitude, up and across the lake and around and around the smoked sky, in an ecstasy of freedom.

"Honk-woak-back!"

And obediently the young banked in the sun, wings stiffening to break the heavy landing. They skidded a bit in the water, then lined up in formation again, impatient for the starting signal.

When I edged down through the dry bushes to the south of the lake, my four — Tiny and Sally, Pedro and Joe — wheeled toward me noisily. They landed out in the deep water, then swam over the shrinking shallows and darted through the cattails, to talk to me. They were so eager to tell me about their joy! Little Tiny climbed up on my boot, flopping her wings against my legs, almost as if she was showing me.

I stooped to stroke them each in turn, and then from the middle of the lake came Old Abraham's stern and strident command, angry in its undertones.

"Honk-woak—" and the deafening, stirring clang that rolled deep into the silent hills. He was telling them the time for play was over. The days for stern discipline had come.

Obediently, my four young honked back, their voices still without the trumpet note. They looked up at me, intelligent black eyes shining — unable to comprehend why their loyalties should be divided.

"Go on, little ones, back to your soloing," I said to them, each in turn. "I understand. After all, I found my own wings once."

Soon there were unmistakable signs of fall in the air. The orange-tipped flies and the big black mosquitoes were gone. Strong dry winds broke what sedges the geese hadn't trampled. One morning the hills to the east were visible through the thinning trees. And it was getting chilly in the tent at night. With an ax, I began throwing up a notched-log cabin, using rocks for a fireplace and a slope of dirt and boughs for the roof. But not for one minute was I unconscious of the waterfowl starting to go south, high chains and arrowheads in the dry blue skies again. The ducks were thinning on Moon Lake, but not a goose had left — on account of Old Abraham's wing, you see. By this time all the young adults were taking long flights daily, filling the sky with bugling — the real sign of their coming of age.

Then, one day, there was an emergency session. Old and young alike were lined up in the middle of the lake like a troop of honour on a runway. Abraham and his family were at the north end, and you could see this was a grave moment.

Old Biddy, this time, sounded the take-off call. The eight of them swam like mad, spattered with their feet, lifted with their wings — but only seven of them got into the air. Abraham's left wing just wouldn't support his weight.

The reaction of those geese almost unnerved me. The old ganders — the flight guides, I had them figured as — honked and conferred, seemingly like they were encouraging Old Abraham not to let this thing get him down.

The geese huddled all that day, and with the next morning they were trying it again. For a whole week, they encouraged and rallied Old Abraham, but it was just no use.

Finally, on a day when the wind was tearing the last leaves

off the scrub and making madcaps on the water, and the Canadas were honking to other geese passing high over the ridge, I heard the greatest gander clang in all the world. That day, even with the wind, it would have deafened a bull moose bellowing.

Right away, those agitated geese lined up respectfully, the wind pushing their back feathers up; and for an hour, like a king battleship — head up, voice strong — Old Abraham tacked and wheeled in their midst. I presume he was appointing a new flock leader and sort of taking farewell of all the old guard who'd flown with him.

At the last, he swam in front of his family, taking leave of them one by one. Each answered him respectfully.

Then he went to his old mate — remember I told you wild geese mate but once — and they rubbed white cheeks together and conferred a while.

Then he swam strongly to the rear, and all the geese on the lake began to regroup.

This time, another she-goose gave the take-off order. The ganders flapped and rose, the young followed, the females taking off last. They circled the lake and formed into a broken arrow-head formation — a sure sign they're going someplace.

They flew south over the ridge, then suddenly the new lead gander turned and they circled back over the lake, flying low.

"Honk-woak-honk!" It was their gesture of farewell to Old Abraham.

The old gander watched them, motionless, long after I couldn't see them any longer.

I called over to him then. I told him that, together, we'd make out all right. That I'd keep a clear spot chopped in the ice all winter. That in the spring his flock would return, and his wing would be okay again.

But it seemed he didn't want any of me then. He looked at me oddly, almost as if seeing me for the first time. Then he swam southwest across the lake, stretching his wings and tucking them against his sides, and disappeared into the broken reeds.

"Three weeks later," said Kirby, beside me on the grounds of the Cavu Club, "they came in."

"I was settling down to a roast of young moose when I heard the motor right smack across the middle of the lake. I'd almost forgotten my pile of signal wood, but I didn't really need a fire. They saw me running down the slope."

Kirby fished in his pocket. "You know, it's funny, but when they gave me this, I felt like a forgotten old man who's just got a letter from one of his kids."

He handed me a small piece of aluminum, easily rolled. I held it up to the light. Three words were punched on it, as if with a shingle nail. KIRBY — MOON LAKE. And at the bottom there was a small "t".

"I banded all six of the young, as well as the two old ones," Kirby said. "This is the only tag turned in; they got it when they picked up some geese for banding, on the Wildlife Refuge, near Herrin, Illinois. You know, I often think those little geese understood what I tried to do. They're so intelligent, you know. Those four will never forget me as long as they live. That's just the way geese are."

I cleared my throat hesitantly. "This small 't' — what does that stand for?"

"Eh?" Kirby had been listening again. "Oh! I put the initials of my four on their tags. That was little Tiny's band — the one who used to sit on my shoe."

I returned the tag to Kirby. He put it in his pocket, carefully, and strolled back to the shadows.

I went into the Club.

Mike Farrell was over at the counter, finishing a Denver with pickles. He was Kirby's buddy — the pilot they sent in to bring him out. Farrel had been stranded for ten days himself once.

I sat beside him and ordered coffee.

"Kirby told me the story," I said. "It's hard to believe."

"It's true, all right." Farrell carefully speared a pickle. "We had the devil's own time getting him to come with us — said he had to stay there and keep the ice open for some bloody great gander. Insisted he was in good shape — and he was, physically."

Farrell got to his feet. "He showed us the coop and the old nest — even tried to get the gander to come out of the reeds for us. It's pretty hard to understand, unless you've been down yourself.

"That's why," he said meaningly, "nobody ever tells Red the truth about that tag. It wasn't taken off in a banding station at all. A farm kid near Vulcan shot the young goose out of a flock in a wheat field. His dad turned the tag over to the RCMP. It told quite a story to us. We asked all concerned to co-operate on where the tag came from — just as a precaution. A thing like that might make an awful difference to a guy's recovery. To Red, those little geese were like his own family then."

The Fall Sun
Bill van Veelen

The fall sun
lands on yellow hills of ripened wheat,
a giant patchwork quilt
covering the land.

A lonely country road
disappears into the dust
from the back of a farmer's pickup,
rusted and dirty.

Old houses, now abandoned, have stories to tell
of the people who used to live there

until the rains didn't come
and they moved to the city.

Old people stare amazed
at the new red Massey-Ferguson
proudly displayed in the farmyard,
muddy and brown.

Down the road farther
lies a small town,
and the word "rush"
is not in its vocabulary.

In the general store and gas station,
ladies gather to gossip, while the men
load 45 gallon drums of gasoline
into the backs of their trucks.

This is the land I know,
it lies down the country road.

Lost At Sea
Maurice Metayer

Nearly a hundred years ago, a group of seal hunters built their igloos at the shore of the ocean in what is known today as Stapylton Bay.

An expanse of solid ice ran from the shore well out into the sea. One day when the weather was favourable a party of men set out, as was their custom, in search of the *aglu,* the breathing holes made by the seals in the sea ice.

When they were some distance from land, the ice suddenly split between the men and the land and a vapour as thick as smoke escaped from the crevasse. Some of the hunters who were closer to the shore had time to jump to the solid ice on the other side before it was too late. However the others who were further out on the ice did not sense the danger as they were concentrating on the *aglu,* waiting for the seal to appear. It was only when one of the men, Ulukhaq, left his place in search of another *aglu* that the crevasse was noticed. Ulukhaq spotted the column of vapour and knew immediately what had happened.

The others heard him cry. "The fog is coming, the mist is rising, the ice is broken!" Calling to one another, all of the hunters ran toward the line of dark smoke which hung like a curtain between themselves and the land.

The men followed the edge of the crevasse, searching in vain for a block of ice which would take them across the water. But the thickening fog hid everything. It was not even possible to attract the attention of those who had escaped to the solid ice on the other side. After a long search, the small group of hunters met together. One of them, Kudlaluk, was missing. His companions thought that he had perhaps found safe passage to the other side and so their hopes were raised.

Just then, however, Kudlaluk reappeared. He had been unable to find a way across the crevasse. The men were forced to stay where they were and soon their ice floe was drifting into the fog where nothing could be seen. That evening the men built an igloo on the ice floe and spent the night in its shelter and warmth.

The next day their ice raft ceased drifting. The hunters found that they were west of their point of departure for they could faintly distinguish the place where their first igloos had been built on the solid ice. Their plan was to stay where they were for the entire day in order to give the newly formed ice between themselves and the mainland time to thicken. All of the men were in agreement with this except Nulialik who wanted to try and reach the shore immediately.

After some discussion, they decided to follow Nulialik. Darkness had fallen. Rather than leave the igloo through its proper entrance they made a hole in the wall large enough to crawl through. The hunters hoped to avoid the evil spirits who were watching the entrance to their igloo and who were undoubtedly responsible for their present problems. Once the passage through the wall was completed the men ran without stopping onto the ice floes, jumping here and there on the more solid chunks of ice.

Closer and closer they came to the safety of the shore. Yet with only a short distance to go the men were stopped. A large crevasse appeared before them and reluctantly the men returned to the igloo from which they had just departed. Here they remained for the better part of the winter.

During these days the men were never far from great danger. Had these been ordinary men they probably would have been lost without hope, but among them there were real *angatkut* or shamans who possessed extraordinary magical powers. Two of the shamans where Qorvik and Kudlaluk.

On one occasion, as the ice raft carrying the men was being drawn toward the west, a large ice pack bore down on top of them and threatened to crush the hunters' igloo. Qorvik used his great shamanistic powers to prevent this disaster by simply leaning against the wall of ice and thereby restraining it.

An ever present threat was the lack of the life-sustaining necessities. Hunger, thirst and the biting cold were constant companions. The snow upon which the men depended for their water supply was now saturated with salt. A burning thirst and the scarcity of food weakened the hunters to the point where their bodies were little more than skin and bones. Obviously something would have to be done if starvation and death were to be averted.

Fortunately, the shamans knew how to stop the disagreeable winds and currents. The shamans knew that the spirits who live on the ocean floor love metal objects. What could be done to please the spirits? Each hunter possessed a long-bladed, raw copper knife — a weapon which never left his side. Without it a hunter on a long journey would risk hunger if not certain death. Perhaps their fortunes would improve if they were to make a gift of the knives to the spirits.

Thus the decision was made. One after another each man sacrificed his knife. Each valued weapon was decorated with a tassel made from thin strips of skin. Then the knife was held over the surface of the water and allowed to sink to the bottom of the ocean. Still all of this was in vain and the men and their ice pack continued to drift, moving ever westward.

One knife still remained, that belonging to Qingalorqana. This knife had a beautiful raw copper blade, highly prized by its owner who was reluctant to give it up. But seeing that there was no other hope, Qingalorqana decided to follow the example set by his companions. Motioning to his friends to gather around, he held the knife over the surface of the clear water. When it left Qingalorqana's hand the hunters were astonished to see this solid copper weapon float for a long period of time. Eventually, it disappeared from sight. Everyone took this to be a good sign; the spirits must be pleased.

Just to be certain that all would be well Qorvik performed one more magic rite. Selecting a small block of ice which the ocean had washed onto their floe, Qorvik threw it in the direction of the land. As he did so he asked the spirits to return them safely to their homes. Shortly thereafter the wind changed direction and the men knew that they were now moving toward safety.

That night the men remained in their igloo, talking among themselves and all the while waiting for the sound of the ice grinding upon the land, the sound that would signal the end of their ordeal.

The next morning land was sighted. Excitedly, the two eldest hunters cried out, "Let's go! Let's go!" One after another the men scrambled out of the igloo with Qorvik in the lead and Kudlaluk bringing up the rear.

In the faint light of the early dawn only the merest outline of the ice floe could be seen. This did not deter the men. Running and jumping from ice block to ice block the hunters made their way toward the shore. All day they worked their way through the pack ice before them. As night was beginning to close in they reached the thick ice that lined the land edge. The men were out of danger at last.

Immediately upon reaching the land the hunters stopped to quench their thirst. The pure snow that they now put into their mouths confirmed in the minds of the men that the salt-saturated snow was behind them. "There is no doubt that we have arrived. This is old, solid ice; it is land!" They shouted with joy as they ate the snow; they laughed and they cried.

They now knew where their igloos were situated and after resting they set out to be reunited with their families. Some paused along the way while others kept moving. In this manner the hunters arrived at their igloos one after another.

A storm was blowing up when they arrived. One man was outside re-covering his igloo in order to make it warm. It was he who heard the noise made by the returning hunters. As soon as he recognized the men he started to jump with joy as one would rejoice after a good hunt. Everyone emerged from their igloos and let loose a joyous howl. They had believed the men lost for good. Some of the women had even taken new husbands. But now that the hunters had returned safely everyone was overcome with happiness.

For a long time thereafter, whenever the hunters would lie down to sleep, the roll of the ocean still rocked their bodies. It became part of their souls and haunted them like a ghost.

Legacy Defaulted
Denise Fair

As I walk into the room, I look around. This is the room where my father was born, where he spent his first three years, and I am hoping to find something that will tell me what he was like when he lived here. My grandparents had taken the family and moved to a bigger house when this one grew too small for them. There seems, at first, to be nothing in the room except dust, but then in the corner, I see something, and walk over to examine it.

There are five blocks set one on top of another, with more scattered around the tower. They are small, about an inch square, with letters of the alphabet painted on them. The letters can hardly be seen any more. Lifting one off the floor to examine it more closely, I realize that it's one of the set my father told me about.

He had told me, when I was a boy, of the days when he was young. He had talked about the only memory of living in this old house that he had. It was moving day, and he had been puzzled, not understanding what was happening, but when he sat down to play with his letter blocks, the world grew still around him, and he became calm. He told me that he never knew what had become of the set.

Now I know. I can see a picture before me of a small three year old, confused by all the activity around him, sitting down to play with the one familiar thing pulled from the packing boxes, a set of blocks. I can see him picking up five blocks, placing them one on top of another, very carefully, so that they are exactly centered. He was always very meticulous.

They are like that still; the bottom four set precisely on top of each other. But the fifth one is over on the right, only half on the tower. Perhaps it had been knocked accidentally by a small hand as the boy left to answer his mother's call. He had to go, and he left his blocks as they were, thinking he would be back in a few minutes to play again.

He had never come back. Later, the house had become his, but it was not the structure he owned; it was the memory. Maybe he felt that if he came back, the memory would be gone, and all he would have left would be an old abandoned shell of a building.

Looking around now, I see that the boy has gone. He left

the house to me, but not the memories. I had thought that this house would give me the key that would open the locked doors of his past, and the memories would be mine also. But the key left with the boy.

120 Miles North of Winnipeg
Dale Zieroth

My grandfather came here years ago,
family of eight. In the village,
nine miles away, they knew him as
the German and they were suspicious, being
already settled. Later he was
somewhat liked; still later
forgotten. In winter everything
went white as buffalo bones and
the underwear froze on the line
like corpses. Often the youngest
was sick. Still he never thought
of leaving. Spring was always greener
than he'd known and summer had
kid-high grass with sunsets big
as God. The wheat was thick,
the log house chinked and warm.
The little English he spoke
he learned from the thin grey lady
in the one-room school, an hour away
by foot. The oldest could hunt, the youngest
could read. They knew nothing of
the world he'd left and forgotten,
until 1914 made him an alien and
he left them on the land he'd come to,
120 miles north of Winnipeg.

The Chinese Café
Ed Arrol

There is one in nearly every town and village in Western Canada, and anybody raised on the prairies has affection for a Chinese café and the gentleman from China who runs it.

Early memories of the "Rex" or "Royal" at Blairmore, Alberta; the "New York" or "Fat's Bum Coffee" at Bassano, where Fat's was recommended by salesmen as serving the best cup of coffee in southern Alberta — brings visions of penny candy and bubble gum, fire crackers and sunflower seeds. When the teens are reached the memories of a Chinese Café include strawberry sodas and chocolate milk shakes and, in winter after skating, cups of hot chocolate.

The working youth will call for a slab of Boston cream pie and a cup of coffee and he will play the jukebox for his girl friend when they drop in to the café for a soft drink or an ice cream float after the show is out.

But whatever the name of the café or the occasion, you might find anyone or anything at "The Chinaman's".

There is colour and romance, noise and friendliness in a Chinese café of Western Canada. Its patrons feel at home there, whether they are calling, "Gimme another piece of pie, Charlie," or having a "chin wag" on a Saturday night.

In communities with towns off the main highways the cafés will be older buildings, usually two stories, with ROOMS FOR RENT upstairs. Most Chinese cafés are big — like the proprietor's heart — and the earlier buildings still have Station Agent or Pot Bellied stoves inside the door while heat from the kitchen warms the back area. As natural gas service comes to more and more prairie towns coal scuttles and shovels disappear when a gas ring is fitted into each stove.

A large showcase of heavy glass displays candy and tobacco just inside the double door, its surface worn and scratched with the passage of coins over the years. Near it is a cash register and its spike holds meal chits. Extending to the kitchen is a long counter where patrons step up and onto stools.

Mirrors may reflect shelves of cream pies and doughnuts and cakes, razor blades and pencils. Often the length of the counter prevents the diner from seeing everyone and it is necessary to walk past the stools on one side and coats hanging along a partition on the other before he can satisfy a curiosity to know "who's in town?"

A visitor from England might think the booths that line both sides of the café, parallel to the counter, are modelled after English railway coaches, for the booths are made long to seat families. Table tops are porcelain (or imitation), in white for easy cleaning. The standard equipment at one is a sugar bowl or shaker, salt and pepper shakers, a bottle each of catsup and sauce, a dispenser of paper napkins, and the inevitable box of salted crackers.

What the menu lacks in imagination is made up in generous servings and the food is piping hot. A glass of cold water is followed by a bowl of steaming soup. Two slices of white and brown bread appear with a pat or two of butter. Next on the menu is something fried with a scoop of mashed potatoes — all smothered in gravy. Dessert with the meal includes a choice of rice pudding, prunes or ice cream. Listed as "extra" are pastries. The call for "apple pie à la mode" or raisin pie with ice cream" is popular. Tea or coffee or milk follows to complete a meal that is common fare at "The Chinaman's", unless he is requested by discriminating eaters to furnish Chinese food.

Newer Chinese restaurants like the Redwater Café in the oil boom town north of Edmonton glitter like a palace under their multicoloured neon lights. The horseshoe coffee bar wends like a snake with its pearl-grey-topped counter, its red-plush stools, its music box that fascinates in a rainbow of colours and is seldom silent. The café opens at six o'clock and closes the following morning at one o'clock — most Chinese cafés have a long day. Chinese food is a specialty and patrons are invited to meet their friends at the café.

Nowadays a visitor to a Chinese café is likely to see the proprietor, between rush hours, doing his bookkeeping with a small adding machine, or pecking out a menu on a portable typewriter. But it is still possible to surprise the owner when he is casting up his accounts on the ancient abacus or see one of the waitresses writing the menu by hand.

The Chinese in Canada have come a long way from days when they helped as members on labour gangs in construction and as workers on the railroads to open up the West. Succeeding generation have started restaurants, laundries and general stores.

In a community in southern Alberta, the United Church was filled to capacity when a Chinese general merchant, there for twenty-six years, died recently.

"He was highly regarded in the district," the obituary notice read, "where he had helped out many a poor family during the period of the depression in the early thirties."

By kindness, patience and hard work they have endeared themselves to their chosen communities.

Buffalo Lake

Ella Elizabeth Clark

In the early days the Sarcee tribe was big. One fall when they were in the Red Deer country, two young men went out to hunt buffalo. Quite a long distance from their camp they saw a buffalo bull standing in a dry valley.

"How can we get a close shot at him?" one young man asked the other.

"Let's chase him," answered the other. "We cannot reach him from here with our bows and arrows."

So they chased the buffalo bull and killed him. Then they began to butcher him, to get the skin and the meat.

"You cut his legs off," one hunter said, "and I will cut him open."

So the man cut off the front legs and one of the hind legs, while the other cut the buffalo open. As he finished, water began to come out of the body, just as a running spring comes out of the side of a mountain.

The men stopped their work and watched. When they saw that the stream continued to flow, they went up on a hill and sat there to watch it. Soon water covered the buffalo's body. Then it began to fill up the little hollow place where the animal had fallen when they killed it. Soon it formed a pool in the shape of a buffalo. A little stream ran out from the place that looked like the tail.

The men watched from the hill until evening. By that time the water had become a large lake, still in the shape of a buffalo. Some willow trees which had been there for a long time now stood beside the part that looked like a head. So the buffalo-shaped lake seemed to have hair.

Late in the evening the hunters returned to camp and told their people about the strange happening and the new lake. Next morning, very early, all the people went with the two men, to see the sight. Sure enough, there was a big lake, in the shape of a buffalo. A stream ran from its tail; and at the spine, where the water was very deep, the animal was deep blue.

Then the people moved on farther north to continue the buffalo hunt. When winter came and it was time to go south again, the head man of the tribe learned that the new lake was frozen over.

"Let's travel south over the new lake," he said to his people. "We can save time by going across it instead of around it."

So they packed their things on horses and on travois and

started across the lake. When some of them had crossed to the opposite side, and some were on the lake, a little boy saw a bone sticking out of the ice.

"I would like to have that bone," he said to his grandmother, who was walking with him. "Will you get it for me?"

"It is the horn of a buffalo," said his grandmother.

She took her axe and began pounding the horn with it, trying to break it off.

All the people near her stopped their horses and their dogs to watch the grandmother. She pounded and pounded, there where the horn touched the ice. Suddenly a big cracking noise startled everyone, as the ice split wide open. Indians, horses, dogs — all that were on the lake fell in and were drowned. Only the people on the shores, those who had crossed over and those who had not yet started, were saved, from all the band of Sarcees.

That is how the Sarcees got divided. Those in the north became known as Beaver and Chipewyan. Those in the south kept the name of Sarcee. The Beaver Indians speak the same language, except that they talk faster than the Sarcees do.

When you pass Buffalo Lake in the evening, you can hear dogs barking and children playing and shouting down in the bottom of the lake. They are the ones that fell through the ice, long, long ago.

Potlatch in the Park
James K. Nesbitt

The log fire burned eerily bright on the earth floor in the centre of the great log house, and the sparks spiralled up to the opening in the roof, and there was smoke in the eyes and fascinating rhythm in the ears. The four old chiefs chanted and beat time with sticks on a bench, and the masked and costumed dancers swayed about the fire and stamped their bare feet on the cold, damp earth. The smoke floated into the air in mild waves, and the firelight cast flickering shadows on the walls and the dim, far-away ceiling; the dancers seemed as though shaken with frenzy; the chant of the old chiefs became louder and louder, more impassioned, and an ancient woman, heavily lined of face, became carried away by it all, back through the years to her childhood. She seemed as if in a spell and then she, too, beat time with her hands and her feet, blind to all around her, but seeing all that the scene meant to her.

It was a potlatch in the new Kwakiutl Indian house in Victoria's famed Thunderbird Park, hard by the Legislative Buildings and the Empress Hotel.

The potlatch was a tremendous success. It was given four times — privately for the Indians and a few anthropologists; for a group of specially invited guests — Mayor Claude Harrison of Victoria and cabinet ministers; twice for the general public. The public almost stampeded. One night nearly 2,000 people lined up for blocks, two and three deep, but couldn't get in. The new house holds only 300 people. Mayor Harrison immediately said Victoria should have a genuine Indian village, that the potlatch should become part of Victoria's uniqueness and culture.

Provincial Government anthropologist Wilson Duff was more than delighted. For it uncovered as he said "a wealth of native dances and a knowledge of traditions we didn't know existed — and it showed just how colourful they can be and what amazing public interest this sort of thing arouses. It made us realize we haven't been doing justice to this part of our local background."

The host at the potlatch was 74-year-old Mungo Martin, a Kwakiutl chief, who has been engaged by the government to carve new totems and to restore the old ones, which had been decaying in Thunderbird Park. So historically priceless are these poles that eventually they'll be stored inside and replicas erected in the park. Wind and rain and insects have been taking their toll.

The new Indian house, the centrepiece of the park, is authentic Kwakiutl, patterned after the house in which Mungo Martin was born at Fort Rupert, on the northeast coast of Vancouver Island. The style of construction, the carved houseposts, the huge adzed beams, the adzed cedar timbers and planks, the house-front painting — all are similar to those of houses built during the 19th century by the Kwakiutl tribes of northern Vancouver Island, and the adjacent mainland. Some concessions had to be made for permanence — concrete footings, steel supports, and some other unseen features.

The Fort Rupert house, after which the Thunderbird Park house was patterned was built about a century ago by a chief with the name which Mungo Martin has since inherited — Naka'penkim. The original house was much larger, but it was of the same general construction, and bore the same carvings on its houseposts. The right to use these carved crests passed to Mungo Martin when he assumed the name several years ago. This, then, is more than just a copy of a Kwakiutl house. It is the house of Chief Naka'penkim of the Ma'mtagila clan of the Kwakiutl tribe.

So it came about that the potlatch which captivated the people of Victoria and excited anthropologists — including several from the University of Washington — was a form of house-warming, a very important event for a large group of Indians who gathered from many parts of Vancouver Island. But a number of the Indians present didn't know what it was all about, any more than did their white-faced brothers and sisters.

Wilson Duff explained that, "the local Indians (Coast Salish) who were invited did not understand the speeches in the Kwakiutl language. Also, they had never seen masks like these before. The interpreter had to explain it to them, as well as to the whites. Mungo Martin had to bring in officials and dancers from the Kwakiutl tribe, and they came from Alert Bay, Fort Rupert, Blunden Harbor, and Quatsino. Inside the house these Kwakiutls were at home; outside they were in a strange land.

"The first day (Indian day) was a real potlatch. The door was closed to all whites except a small number of anthropologists, whom Mungo specially invited, so that this last great potlatch would be thoroughly recorded. Solemn ceremonies preceded the main dances; the singing of mourning songs for recently deceased relatives (for winter dances cannot be performed until the tears are wiped from the eyes); and the ceremonial change-over to winter dance organization, and the distribution of the red cedar bark head-rings symbolizing the winter dance season. Then the winter dances could begin!"

To the Indians of coastal British Columbia, completion of a new house was a most important event that called for great ceremonies and feasting. At such a house warming, the owner must prove his hereditary right to use the carved and painted crests on the houseposts and the house-front, by relating his family traditions and accomplishments. He is expected to "potlatch" gifts to those who helped him build the house, and to the important guests who have come to witness the ceremonies. He usually takes the opportunity to bestow important inherited names on members of his family, and to display the masked dances and other performances which belong to himself, or members of his family by virtue of inheritance or marriage.

All this, Mungo Martin explained to his guests, speaking in his native language, but with the aid of an interpreter.

David Martin, Mungo's son, took part in the dances. He later recalled potlatches he had danced in when he was a boy. He laughed as he remembered them. Why, he said, sometimes they lasted for a month, sometimes two months. The youngsters had a wonderful time. They were always doing things they weren't supposed to do. Potlatch-time, to the boys and girls, was just like one long party. There was always plenty to eat — dried salmon and berries, now and then a seal, clams by the dozen, and oolachan oil.

Important families had names for their houses. Old Naka'penkim owned two such names, and Mungo Martin chose one of them for his new house in Thunderbird park — Wa'waditla, meaning "he orders them to come inside". That indicates the chief in this house is so all-powerful he can order anybody into his house, to become his servant.

The carvings on the posts which hold up the new Thunderbird Park house are copied from Naka'penkim's old house at Fort Rupert. The back posts have the mythical bird Ho'hoq at the top and the Grizzly Bear at the bottom, holding up a child. The front posts show the giantess Dsonoqua (Emily Carr did one of her finest Indian paintings of this figure) at the top, with Grizzly Bear holding a copper below. Each of these figures represents the origin-legend of one of the clans to which Naka'penkim was related by heredity or marriage.

The long-beaked Ho'hoq, which startled the guests by loudly clapping its beak, was the main crest of the Gi'ksem clan, to which Naka'penkim's wife belonged.

It was customary for the tall, heraldic pole in front of the house to display the crests of the clans to which the owner of the house belonged. The great pole in front of the Thunderbird Park house, however, was carved by Mungo Martin to represent all of the Kwakiutl tribes, and it shows crests of four of them — the Awaitla, Nakoaktok, and Nimpkish, as well as the Kwakiutl proper.

The top figure is Tsoona, the Thunderbird, a crest of the Tsoo'tsuns clan of the Awaitla tribe of Knight Inlet. The original ancestor of this clan was the Thunderbird, who became a man. Later, his son returned to the sky to control thunder and lightning. Next is Wa'walibui the Grizzly Bear ancestor of the Wa'walibui clan of Kwakiutls, and then a man, representing the same being after he became human. Next is the Beaver, Tsw'wa, an ancestor of the Naboaktok tribe of Blunden Harbor, where Emily Carr also painted a magnificent Indian scene. One clan of the Nimpkish tribe has the mythical giantess Dsonoqua as its crest. The bottom figure on the totem pole represents this tradition and shows Dsonoqua holding her son.

After the ceremony was over, Mr. Duff explained something of the history of the Kwakiutl ceremonial dances we saw at the potlatch: "More than all other tribes of the B.C. coast, the Kwakiutl are famous for their masked dances. These dances were performed during a definite season of the winter, when the spirits were thought to return to the villages. The masked figures were the spirits, the whistles were their voices. The persons who were possessed by the same spirit grouped themselves into an order or society. There were many such 'secret societies', but the highest was the Ha'matsa, or Cannibal Society.

"Each dancer had a special winter dance name. In winter, as soon as the cedar bark headbands were donned, symbolizing the start of the dancing season, the summer names were dropped, and the winter names only were used. The great social and ceremonial events of the season were the initiation of young people into the dancing societies. These were open only to persons who obtained the right through inheritance or marriage. The initiations were long and expensive, requiring that the host display his traditional masked dances, and give food and gifts to the guests. Kwakiutl dances and songs, therefore, are owned by individuals. They are passed on by inheritance or marriage, and most of them are associated with the winter dance secret societies."

These, then, were some of the fascinating dances we saw at the potlatch in mid-December. We saw, for instance, Ga'lokwimth, wife of Baxbakwalanuxsiwac, the Kwakiutl Spirit of Cannibalism. This was a huge mask, with clapping, rumbling jaws, a splendid, handsome, quite awesome specimen of Indian totem carving. At the beginning of the program, the long beaks of the Ho'hoq birds at the tops of the poles holding the roof beams snapped for silence among the guests. There was an impressive Yathla, or cradle ceremony. There was a large, carved cradle and four old chiefs chanted and shook their rattles until the baby fell cozily asleep. This ceremony was performed for Dorothy Martin, the granddaughter of Mungo.

There was a realistic bee dance around the flickering fire, done by a child; and the women's dance, the women, too, in bare feet on that cold, damp earthen floor, and as they danced round the fire they scattered eagle-down to show their hopes for peace among all tribes, all nations, all people. Came then the Dance of the Animals — a wolf, a raccoon, a mouse, a kingfisher, a night owl, a marten, a squirrel, a wren, a pair of deer, a wild man. Here was a wonderful spectacle indeed, as brilliant as any ballet, authentic, and filled with Indian history. Nothing had been changed.

There was a spirit of friendliness about the potlatch in Mungo Martin's new house. Those who had thought that potlatches were drunken, frenzied orgies were surprised, and pleased, and wondered why the government had frowned on them.

Sitting in that big house, warmed by the open fire, the smoke in our eyes, the chant in our ears, it seemed impossible to believe it was 1953 and that we were in the heart of busy Victoria. It was easier to imagine that house on some lonely beach far up the coast, one of those long, curving beaches washed by the swells of the Pacific, a beach with Indian dugouts drawn up. We could almost hear the waves washing the pebbles, the sigh of the fir trees over the house, and the lashings of the rain. . . .

Yet there was sadness at that ceremony, for the old chiefs knew that potlatches are going, that the young Indians of today are not much more interested in them than they are in carving totem poles. "There's lots more masks," as one of the old men said, "but there's nobody to wear them."

Nevertheless, the potlatch and the new Kwakiutl house made a deep impression on those who saw them, and many who have scoffed at Indian art and Indian history have found a new interest and a new meaning in them, through the efforts of old Chief Naka'penkim and his anthropologist friends.

The Kiskatinaw Songs
Sean Virgo & Susan Musgrave

Adapted from the songs and mythologies of the British Columbia Indians as told by Moses Bruce of Tlell.

Stranger Song

I have no fear:
Down this street I am
A frog hopping.
I am in the market
For a brother.

They will not touch me:
The wolves crowd at my back
But the frog is mighty,
I thank my mother
For that gift.

Now this house:
He stands out straight
By the doorpost faces.
Stranger brother
With frog tattoos.

In his house

I may eat with my hand in
His hand. His breath
is my food. My song
is his dance.

Wolf people
Come to our doorway showing
Respect. They shuffle
Their feet. So must the bear
At the Frog's house.

Tonight they will wait
For me to dance out first.
They must hop in my
Footsteps. Now I am
Their uncle.

Power of the Frog
On this beach far across
With the strangers' tongues.
I thank my mother
For that gift.

Captive Song

We are crowded in this house,
This chief's son and me.
Soon they will know it,
Soon they will lead us out.

Shaman woman,
My heart is not strong enough!
This chief's son brought me fish —
I cut their eyes out!
Then it was said
For three days we did mischief
In that house.
Shaman woman,

My tongue is not sharp enough!
This chief's son brought me flesh —
I cut the hearts out!
Then it was said
For three days we did mischief
In that house.

We are crowded in here,
How sleepy we are!
Ask this chief's son
To give us his blankets,
To give blankets to the whole world
Against the word of our chief.

Inside Song

Wind from the sea

On the salt marsh
The dead ones clamour
With their cold songs

Wind from the cold sea
Now it is good
Turning to this close woman
She is lying awake

Wind from the sea
Sometimes you make it
Even closer
And safe in here

Sleep

Emily Carr

When I was a child I was staying at one of Victoria's beaches.

I was down on the point watching a school of porpoises at play off Trail Island when a canoe came round the headland. She was steering straight for our beach.

The Government allowed the Indians to use the beaches when they were travelling, so they made camp and slept wherever the night happened to fall.

In the canoe were a man and woman, half a dozen children, a dog, a cat and a coop of fowls, besides all the Indians' things. She was a West Coast canoe — dug out of a great red cedar tree. She was long and slim, with a high prow shaped like a wolf's head. She was painted black with a line of blue running round the top of the inside. Her stern went straight down into the water. The Indian mother sat in the stern and steered the canoe with a paddle.

When the canoe was near the shore, the man and the woman drove their paddles strong and hard, and the canoe shot high up onto the pebbles with a growling sound. The barefoot children swarmed over her side and waded ashore.

The man and the woman got out and dragged the canoe high onto the beach. There was a baby tucked into the woman's shawl; the shawl bound the child close to her body. She waddled slowly across the beach, her bare feet settling in the sand with every step, her fleshy body squared down onto her feet. All the movements of the man and the woman were slow and steady; their springless feet padded flatly; their backs and shoulders were straight. The few words they said to each other were guttural and low-pitched.

The Indian children did not race up and down the beach, astonished at strange new things, as we always were. These children belonged to the beach, and were as much a part of it as the drift-logs and the stones.

The man gathered a handful of sticks and lit a fire. They took a big iron pot and their food out of the canoe, and set them by the fire. The woman sat among the things with her baby — she managed the shawl and the baby so that she had her arms free, and her hands moved among the kettles and food.

The man and a boy, about as big as I was, came up the path on the bank with tin pails. When they saw me, the boy hung back and stared. The man grinned and pointed to our well. He had coarse hair hanging to his shoulders; it was unbrushed and his head was bound with a red band. He had wrinkles everywhere, face, hands and clothing. His coat and pants were in tatters. He was brown and dirty all over, but his face was gentle and kind.

Soon I heard the pad-pad of their naked feet on the clay of the path. The water from the boy's pail slopped in the dust while he stared back at me.

They made tea and ate stuff out of the iron pot; it was fish, I could smell it. The man and the woman sat beside the pot, but the children took pieces and ran up and down eating them.

They had hung a tent from the limb of the old willow tree that lolled over the sand from the bank. The bundles and blankets had been tossed into the tent; the flaps were open and I could see everything lying higgledy-piggledy inside.

Each child ate what he wanted, then he went into the tent and tumbled, dead with sleep, among the bundles. The man, too, stopped eating and went into the tent and lay down. The dog and the cat were curled up among the blankets.

The woman on the beach drew the smouldering logs apart; when she poured a little water on them they hissed. Last of all she too went into the tent with her baby.

The tent full of sleep greyed itself into the shadow under the willow tree. The wolf's head of the canoe stuck up black on the beach a little longer; then it faded back and back into the night. The sea kept on going slap-slap-slap over the beach.

Gregg Cabin
Jody McCurdy

In silence
it sits, waiting
for its
weekend occupants
to arrive

to warm
its chilled
walls
with song
and laughter,
to stoke
its stove
with happiness

Alone
a piece
of civilization
planted
in nothingness.

Provincial
Miriam Waddington

My childhood
was full of people
with Russian accents
who came from
Humble Saskatchewan
or who lived in Regina
and sometimes
visited Winnipeg
to bring regards
from their frozen
snowqueen city.

In those days
all the streetcars
in the world slept
in the Elmwood
car-barns and the
Indian moundbuilders
were still wigwammed
across the river
with the birds
who sang in the bushes
of St. Vital

Since then I have

visited Paris
Moscow London
and Mexico City
I saw golden roofs
onion domes and the
most marvellous
canals, I saw people
sunning themselves
in Luxembourg Gardens
and on a London parkbench
I sat beside a man
who wore navy blue socks
and navy blue shoes
to match.

All kinds of miracles:
but I would not trade
any of them for the
empty spaces, the
snowblurred geography
of my childhood.

I Remember

Terri Kishkan

I remember summer in Matsqui
    with the smell of new mown hay drifting by on the breeze
Hay rides in the evenings
    wagons drawn by huffing puffing tractors
    (driven by someone's little brother)
    and acres of pink clover.
In Matsqui there are creeks made for swimming in
    and railroad tracks made for walking on
    at twilight with your best friend.

Have you ever laid two pennies, one on top of the other,
    on the track and had them squished together
    by the 3:00-to-Mission-train?

I remember Matsqui in the fall
    with harvest of cow-corn
    and late crop hay
    and the apples in the orchard
    where our horse lived.
School and Tom-the-bus-driver
    with his rickety yellow bus
    honking outside every morning
    and porridge,
Music of wind in Langlaar's poplars
    and the final michaelmas daisies
    in the far pasture,

I remember winter in Matsqui
    with cold nor'westers blowing hard across
    the prairie
    snow piled up in house-high drifts by the back door
    and sweet hot molasses to warm the cow's insides
    and mine too,
Snow held us captives from school
    and even our neighbours,
Once, when the roads were clear
    my friend and I made snowballs
    with nails in them so the bus
    would get flat tires
    but it didn't work.
Christmas carols for the cows
    lights on the huge evergreens
    and skating all night.

I remember Matsqui in the spring
    with new calves and

rains leaving impressions
of rainbows in the high sky.
Picnics at the creek with sandwiches and
    gallons of milk
    and trout grinning as they
    swam by our hooks.
New leaves on old trees
    planting the corn and
    chain harrowing the fields
    and then moving away.

Moose Jaw, Saskatchewan
Miriam Mandel

When I was seven
we moved to live
in Moose Jaw, Saskatchewan
which for me
existed
primarily
of the library and Crescent Park.

Crescent Park is hard to descibe
almost unbelievable
in the centre of the city
a park of bark wood bridges
gently sloping
over rivers, streams
where swans swim
and trees bend
to watch
themselves
sway

a reflection
of leaves and flowers
hidden bowers
for lovers
who meet
in this park
about which
what is remarkable
is it
didn't exist
until men
came — built
it.

More remarkable still
than this lovely, dreamy
park built
by
men's
will
out of bare ground
without even water
before
they put it there
is at the entrance of the park
there was something
I had
never seen
a library
and it could be used
by even children
everybody. Me.

Before
I had seen only

twenty, thirty
books at a
time mostly
in school where
finished your work
one
could go to the back
of the room
choose a book
to read.

And now in this city, this park
this library
I was free
to wander up and down
the rows of books
and look, pick
take
home with me
all
these works to be
read all of which
I couldn't
possibly read
but wouldn't give in
to that belief
tried and tried
had
long evenings, long days
nights
with my flashlight
in bed
where I read
and still couldn't believe
so many books

could
be.
I loved, love to read.

But believe
or not
at the very other end
the opposite end of the park
was the natatorium
a place to swim
in summer, in winter
built
over a natural hot spring.

That, too, seemed
miraculous,
both
nature and man
had succeeded in
building
a park, pool, library
all
exquisite
previously
non-existent
in the centre of my small city
Moose Jaw, Saskatchewan.

She Goes Away
Gordon Burles

In front of my darkened house
old trees line the street like
the last days of our togetherness
or like the faltering words of

this note telling why you left.
Sitting on the porch, I read
that at every corner you turned
suddenly you saw roads
leading to London or Paris
and in the morning when you
looked out our window
you thought, "How can I be wed to
a particular house on a particular road?"

Twilight descends on my house
and I try to console myself,
thinking that if you seek to
escape yourself, you never will;
and if you try to escape
the single place, in the end
your life will be engraved on
nothing but the roads. Yet from
time to time I have doubts
for in the heart of a nomad
perhaps something is at peace
and doubtless a wanderer's memory
is his monument. I imagine that
when we are buried in the earth
part of you will try to escape
the tree roots that hold you
and part of me will envy that,
for in your bones will be
the places and ways I only
heard about as they were
described to my house by the wind.

The Prairie

Sid Marty

Now but a bruise on the sidehill,
the sod hut they packed their love into
Little more than desire
kept out the sun and the rain
Not much more than love
did they have
there on the ravished plain

Here is their hard won house
abandoned now
that they built from the roots
coming out of the ground at last
to name every direction they wheeled in
and plant their landmark in the air,
to break the desolate arc
. . . but the name of the house is lost
like them

It is a secret kept by the neighbours
who survived
the politics of wind
and money

They will understand me
knowing how hard it is
to corral the wind

And you strangers
knowing only the highway,
you too
can at least imagine
in that extremity

as any desert
the sole relief of a tree

Hunting grouse
on the old abandoned farm,
we found a crabapple tree
heavy with fruit,
eaten only by deer

How many years ago
did the couple we'll say
were young
windburnt flowers
plant the dozen varieties
of trees

Act of love, to seed the prairie
among the buffalo beans,
the old dream shouldered aside

Sliced the turf, and watered green shoots
from mountain streams flowing
under deep black dirt
under the glacial debris

A thousand beaded pails
carried in the heat of summer
flashing of the metal
by the white alkali sloughs

Crabapples cured by frost taste sweet
tasting of cool nights
moonshine cider,
water, the depths of earth

The flavour of love savoured by strangers
lingers on in red crabapples
Though the passion of this house
has faded like a fiery old woman
hugging the wind in her spaces
beneath the open windows of the sky

Grade Five Geography Lesson
Barry Stevens

Children never get to the point,
They surround it.
The importance of the point
Is the landscape of it.
You begin by discussing "The Rainfall of Vancouver Island"
And somebody has an uncle who lives there.
And there is an uncle in Alberta
Who has a zillion cows,
Some chickens and a horse
(We get to feed the chickens
And ride the horse),
Which brings us to an uncle
In Saskatchewan, who has a house where
Deer pass the kitchen window
Every morning (He takes us out
And shows us where they go).
If there were no uncles on Vancouver Island
It would never rain there.

The Burning
W. D. Valgardson

John Stepanovich was so upset that he walked into the kitchen without knocking the snow from his shoes. He stopped halfway across the floor and said to his wife: "Anna, they are going to burn down the house."

Anna was rolling dough at the cupboard for *peroghi*. She put the rolling-pin down, wiped her hands on her apron and said, "Who would do that?"

"The firemen at the plant."

"Right now?" She asked the question without raising her voice.

Anna was short and squat. Her face was round and one eyelid drooped slightly, a reminder of a small stroke that she had had three years before. She wore a red scarf on her head to keep the drafts from her ears, for she was subject to ear-aches. Sometimes they got so bad that she could feel the roots of teeth that had been pulled out long ago. She wore a loose brown dress that came to her ankles and sturdy, low-heeled shoes.

"Next Monday," John replied.

"Go clean your feet," Anna said, "And shut the door properly. You're letting a draft in and making puddles on the floor."

John looked down. It was true. Hurriedly, he squatted and picked up the lumps of snow that had fallen from his shoes. He took a handful of snow and threw it outside.

John was short and thickset. He was bald except for a light fringe of hair that circled his head just at the tops of his ears. He never let his fringe of hair get ragged. Every Sunday morning before mass he sat in a kitchen chair while Anna snipped at his hair with her scissors. His upper lip was covered with a bushy, drooping moustache. He was proud of his moustache. It still didn't have any grey in it and at weddings and funerals after he had had two or three beers, he would chide the younger men by pointing to their grey hair, and saying, "Humph! Grey hair already. That's not a good sign. Not a grey hair here." He would stroke his moustache with his forefinger and if Anna was close by, say to her, "Not bad for a man over 75."

He pulled the door closed. Some snow had fallen between the aluminum storm door and the frame. He stooped and scratched it out with his finger. When he shut the door again, he said, "Modern doors. If you don't watch, they bend right away and you can't plane them. You didn't have to worry about wooden doors."

He took his jacket off and hung it up. "I was at the Co-op when I heard about it. Everybody was talking."

"Have a cup of coffee," Anna said. She always kept water boiling on the back of the stove during the winter. John started to say something, but she cut him off by taking the instant coffee out of the cupboard and putting a spoonful into a cup. "Sit down and tell me. Do you want to have another heart attack?"

As she gave him his coffee, Anna said, "Why are they going to burn it down?"

John spilled some coffee into his saucer to cool. "For fire practice. They don't want kids using it for parties. They don't want to hire a caretaker. Besides, the fire brigade is going to get a reward for safety."

"So?"

"So. So! They will give a demonstration for the big shots at the Atomic plant. Then they will get their reward. Everything is solved. No parties. No caretaker. Everybody is happy."

John sat rigidly in his chair. The dark, lined skin of his face was flushed.

"Drink your coffee," Anna said, "I have *peroghis* to make for dinner." She went back to the cupboard.

"They can't do it. They have no right. That's your house. I built it for you."

Anna didn't turn from cutting the dough into pieces. "John, it's not ours anymore. That time is gone. This is our house now."

John's hand trembled as he drank his coffee. When he finished, he refilled the saucer. "They are thieves," he said.

Anna rolled some pieces of dough into balls. She put the balls at the back of the cupboard and laid clean dish towels over them. Her legs had begun to hurt so she made coffee for herself and came to the table.

"What will you do?"

"I don't know. I'm an old man. What can an old man do?"

"The lawyer. . . ."

"Ha, the lawyer! I know the lawyer. When they took our house I saw the lawyer. He talks and talks and does nothing. His grandfather was the same. All the Kuzlaks are like that."

"Maybe the priest?"

When John didn't reply, Anna said, "He knows about things. He could talk to someone."

"When the Atomic people came and said they were taking our house and our land, I told the priest to stop them. Instead, he said we had to leave. I said, 'Did God say so?' He is like the rest of them. He wants to be a big shot. They give him a tour of the plant and ask him to say a prayer and he can't do enough for them."

"He's young," Anna said. "We made mistakes when we were young."

"You'd make excuses for the devil." As quickly as he said it, John was sorry. What he said was true, but there were some things better not mentioned. There had been many times he had been glad of Anna's forgiving nature. "I'm sorry," he added, "but he kept making excuses. Why didn't he tell the truth and be finished? He kept saying how old we were getting. He wanted us to be close to a doctor. We might get sick any day. I asked him why no one had worried about us before. Petroskis are living on the ridge. She's been sick for ten years. No one is worrying about them. We'd been there since we were seventeen and sixteen. No one worried when we lost our children. No one came to help me dig the graves."

"John Stepanovich," Anna said, "it is no longer our house. They paid us money. They let us take the apple tree. Next fall, if we live, we will transplant the plum trees."

"But it is not fair," John insisted.

"What is fair, John Stepanovich? We have lived a long time. We came here when we were very young. They gave us land. Now they have taken it away. At least they gave us something in return."

"They are thieves," John cut in angrily. "I cut the timbers

myself. It took me two days to bring the lumber by waggon. In the wet spots I helped the horses pull. They could have let us stay for a year or two. What would it have hurt?"

He stopped, sorry again for what he had said. He put his hand on her arm. "I'm sorry. It is not you I am angry at. Perhaps you are right."

"Maybe the priest could suggest something."

"No, not after the last time. We have passed twice on the street and I haven't spoken. I can't go and beg for help now."

"Maybe the lawyer."

"No," John replied. Then, seeing that Anna's eyes were red, he added, "Maybe." After a moment: "But who would he talk to? It would be like last time. Everybody is sorry, but nobody is to blame."

John put on his parka and went outside. He had farmed all his life. When things went wrong, he needed to work with his hands. Being outside cleared his head and let him think. When he was younger, he sometimes cut a cord of wood without stopping. Now he had to be careful. He still had his strength, but the doctor had warned him about his heart. He didn't care for himself so much, but he didn't want to leave Anna alone. She didn't like to go out in the snow, so he did the shopping during the winter.

It had been snowing all day. The flakes that fell on his jacket were large and clung to him because of his warmth. He pulled his woollen mitts on and brushed the snow off the woodpile. He lifted down a block of birch.

He held the block with one hand. As he split kindling from its side, he turned the block round and round. The birch was frozen. It split cleanly. John worked until his feet started to get cold, then he carried an armload of kindling inside.

Anna was dropping the *peroghi* into a pot of boiling water when he came in. She kept her head down so as not to let him see that she had been crying. The edge of her apron was wet and wrinkled. He shook the snow on his cap into the slop pail.

"I'm going uptown. If I see the priest, I will ask him."

Ever since they had moved into town, John had gone uptown at least once a day. Sometimes he picked up groceries for Anna, but more often he sat in the back of the Co-op store. There, the farmers who were in town for the day gathered around the cases of tinned fruit and the blocks of salt. While their wives shopped in the front of the store, they talked about crops and the cost of machinery. Sometimes one of them brought a sealer of homebrew and they drank it from Seven-up bottles.

This morning there were only two or three women in the store. John walked to the back but no one was there. The snow had kept the farmers at home. Nearly all the men who lived in town worked on highway crews or town maintenance crews. They would be busy all day trying to keep the roads open.

John walked past the lawyer's three times before he went in. When he explained to Kuzlak about the burning of the house, Kuzlak said, "What do you expect me to do? It's their house. They paid for it." When he saw the determined look on John's face, he became exasperated. "The house is over 50 years old. I know you built it with your own hands. But it's just a house, nothing more. A place to stay out of the rain" — he swung his hand toward the window — "and out of the snow. You have a new home, a better home now."

John got up. He didn't offer to shake hands. "The doors bend if you get even a flake of snow on their edge." He didn't bother to wait for Kuzlak's reply.

The priest was in his early twenties. He didn't come from the district and John didn't know his family. He preferred the old priest who had come around for a drink of whisky during the week and always stayed for supper. The new priest was always in a hurry. He never came to a full stop at intersections and he never came for supper. John was sure that, if he did come, he would eat his supper standing up.

In spite of John's not having spoken to him when they passed on the street, the priest was sympathetic. He was sorry that he could do nothing about the fire practice.

John felt lost. If the priest had been like Kuzlak, he could at least have been angry. They sat on each side of the desk in silence, then John said, "The house belonged to my wife. I gave it to her."

When he did not continue, the priest said, "Is she the one who doesn't want it burnt down? What does she say?"

"She says it is theirs. They paid us for it."

The priest nodded. "She is right. It is theirs."

"But I gave it to her." John couldn't think of anything else to say.

"I understand," the priest said, but John could see that he did not. "I understand, but I'm afraid there's nothing I can do. It's really a legal problem."

As John was going out the door, the priest looked up from his papers and said, "Why don't you go to see Kuzlak? He knows about these things."

Thursday and Friday, John stayed at home. Some of their friends stopped by to say they were sorry about the house. More would have come, but it was still snowing. Those who came said it was unfair, but that there was nothing that could be done.

On Saturday morning, John decided to go the the Atomic plant. He put on a white shirt and tie. He took out his black suit that he wore to church and for special occasions like the anniversaries and funerals. He went to the Co-op store and got a ride out to the plant when the Co-op manager was delivering groceries to farmers who lived on the other side of the plant property.

The young man at the gatehouse was very pleasant. He listened politely, then phoned the main building.

When he came back to the front desk, he said, "I'm sorry, but Mr. Erickson is who you want to see and he's in Ottawa right now. He won't be back until Monday morning."

John stood there. He didn't know what to do. The young man said, "I'm sorry, but there's nothing anyone else can do." He opened the door for John. John thanked him and left.

John walked to the main highway. Just before the plant road and the highway joined, he stopped to look through a windbreak of pines. He couldn't see the house so he stepped onto the driveway. The snow was up to his knees.

He walked a little way in so that he could see a corner of the house. It wasn't much to look at. The house only had four rooms, but it had a good basement. Even though he had to dig it by hand, John had made the basement deep. He had been proud of the basement because they could both stand up in it. Most of the other basements in the district had been so shallow that they were nothing more than root cellars. Because of the snow that had drifted against the house, John couldn't see the basement, but he didn't need to. He had dug the earth, built the frame and poured the concrete by hand. When they were forced to leave, the basement still didn't have a crack in it. He had built the house to last.

The wood siding was yellow. In a way he was grateful for the overcast and the screen of trees. It meant he couldn't see where the paint had begun to peel, or where the teenagers had scrawled their names on the siding.

The plum trees were close to the front door. The fire wouldn't hurt them, but the snow-removal crews and the spectators would snap the brittle branches.

The trees had been grown from plum seeds. Anna had planted ten seeds. Only two had grown, but they had always produced lots of plums. The plums were not as big and sweet as the plums in the store, but they were much bigger and sweeter than the wild plums.

He was still standing in the driveway when the Co-op manager pulled up beside him. The manager honked his horn. John looked up, raised his hand in greeting, then turned and walked to the truck.

On Sunday morning John and Anna went to mass. After they came home, they had hot apple-juice and cinnamon to chase away the cold. Anna did some sewing while John sat at the kitchen table playing solitaire and smoking his pipe. Twice during the afternoon, he went outside and split wood.

After supper he put on his galoshes and parka. "I'll be back in a little while," he said. "Maybe I'll go and play some penny cribbage."

Anna nodded. He often spent Sunday evening playing cribbage. If he was winning, he sometimes didn't get home until after midnight. She didn't object. The owner of the cafe locked the doors at six o'clock and three or four of the men played in the back booth. John was sensible. He always quit when he was 50 down.

John was in the front yard when Anna banged on the window. He had forgotten the black purse in which he kept his pennies. He came back and got it from her.

He walked toward the cafe until he couldn't be seen from the house. Then he turned toward the highway. It wasn't snowing anymore, but the temperature had dropped to ten below. John didn't try to hurry. The snow-clearing crew wouldn't start work on the driveway to Anna's house until early in the morning. That way, even if it started to snow again, the driveway would be clear for the morning's fire practice.

His breath made long white plumes. He swung his arms and flexed his fingers so they would stay warm. He had four miles to walk.

He was about halfway there when his heart began to beat too quickly. He slowed down. There was no hurry. He stopped and rested at the end of the next mile.

When he reached the junction, he looked at his pocket watch. 7:30. It had taken him an hour and a half. Even five years before he could have walked the same distance in half the time. He rested again just inside the driveway. There was no chance of his being seen, for the windbreak of spruce hid him from anyone who might drive by.

He climbed the stairs and kicked the snow away from the bottom of the door. A small padlock had been placed over the handle. He took a hammer from his pocket and pulled the latch off the door. The inside of the house was dark. He turned on his flashlight.

He opened the cellar door. He played the light along the stairs. They still looked sturdy, but someone had left large hunks of mud on the bottom two stairs. He didn't need to go down. There was a cistern, the furnace, a wood chute and shelves he had put up for Anna's preserves.

He went into the kitchen and ran his hands over the cupboards. The joints were still tight, the surface smooth. He was not a carpenter, but his work was good.

He opened the doors to the bedrooms, then he went back to the kitchen. He couldn't draw himself away from the cupboards. He ran his hand along their edge and thought about Anna. He could still remember what she had looked like when she was sixteen. There was no drooping eye then. When she worked, she was quick and efficient. Even if she stood at the cupboards all day, her legs didn't hurt her. Her hair had been lighter, like the colour of tanned deer hide. When he came in from the fields he had run his hands through it. For a minute, John imagined that Anna was with him, leaning against the cupboard and laughing as he caught her in his arms.

He opened the cupboard doors. The shelves were lined with newspapers. He pulled the papers loose and threw them into the bottom cupboard.

When he had stripped the last shelf, he took out his pipe. He had filled it with tobacco before he left. He tamped the tobacco down with his finger.

He fished a match from his parka pocket and struck with his thumbnail. The match flared. He sucked the flame into the bowl of his pipe, then bent down and touched the flame to the edge of a newspaper.

At first the paper burned slowly because of the cold. John

stepped back to the doorway as more paper caught fire. When the wood was crackling and he could smell the linoleum beginning to burn, he pulled on his mitts.

He didn't hurry on the way home. The windows of the house had been boarded up. It would be a while before anyone would see the flames. The sky had cleared and he could see the big dipper. It was going to get colder.

Anna was in bed when he got home. She had left a pan on the stove with lemonade and cinnamon. He mixed in two ounces of whisky and drank it as he warmed his feet and hands. Before he turned off the kitchen light, he put some briquets into the stove.

As he was undressing, Anna woke and said, "Did you fix the fire?"

"Yes," he said, "the fire will be fine."

"Did you win at cribbage?"

"No," he said. "But I didn't lose either."

He could hear Anna roll over in bed. "That's not so bad then."

"No," John replied as he pulled the covers over himself, "that's not so bad."

Wild Man's Butte

Anne Szumigalski & Terrence Heath

The text of "Wild Man's Butte" is set up for stereophonic production. The letters A to E indicate the place in stereophonic space from which the voice or sounds originates. Graphically, these places may be indicated as follows:

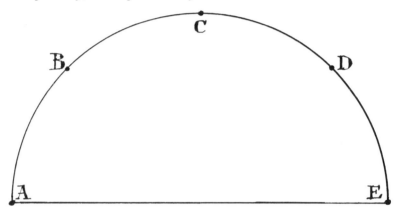

The piece is designed for only natural sound effects, except for the two Indian songs, and background silence.

Voices: NARRATOR

HENRI BEAUBIER — junior surveror

TOM GREENAWAY — senior surveyor

AYEE — young Indian woman

(SUMMER ELECTRICAL STORM, PEALS OF THUNDER, ECHOING, NO RAIN, NO WIND, BEGINS AT "A" AND MOVES THROUGH TO "E" IN THE COURSE OF THE OPENING SPEECH)

NARRATOR: At the beginning of time before time,
(at "C")   There was the earth, and there was the sky,
              The sky cracked in a chaos of thunder
              Lightning ringed the valleys,
              Crashing on the circling hills,

Splitting open the white sky like rocks,
Out of this light came man, the warrior,
Looking far to the North and South, to the West
And East for game; measuring the distance
Of his stride on the hilltops. The cleavages of
Boulders were his only house. His shoulders
His only strength.
                    Out of the earth,
Out of the treed coulees cut in the prairie floor
Came woman, the preparer,
Seeking and finding a use for fire, and making
Ready herbs and berries, roots, seeds
And bark, the salt of lake beds,
The mineral of rocks, the lichen and even soil
For the time when they might be needed.
She pressed her spittle into animal hides
And tanned soft garments in the fire's smoke.

The man called down to her huddled on the edge
Of a lake, rocking herself in the acrid smell,

MAN: "Woooooomaaaaaaaannnnnnn! Come,
(at "A")   Bring me up a sinew for my bow."

NARRATOR: The woman turned her head away, and whispered:
(at "C")

WOMAN: "Man, you come down here. And bring me the
(at "E")   sky."

NARRATOR: She took the longest and toughest thong she had
(at "C")   And, holding tight to one end, threw it skyward.
              He grasped it, but she did not let go.
              She pulled with all the strength prepared in her
              And toppled the mighty warrior from the butte.
              Man fell from the sky like a star
              And lay screaming at her feet.

MAN: "You she-devil,
(at "A")   You source of deceit."

WOMAN: But, Lord, do you not see that my sinew is strong
(at "E")   and good?"

(STORM RUMBLES AWAY AND THERE IS SILENCE. THE SILENCE COULD LAST
AS LONG AS THREE SECONDS. THEN, WIND COMES UP AND NARRATOR BEGINS
TO SPEAK. WIND DOES NOT RISE ABOVE MEDIUM AND FLUCTUATES)

NARRATOR: At the beginning of time, about 1910
(at "D")   When the surveyors came and pricked
             The dried scabs of prairie with their rods,
             At that time, the butte had no name;
             It was a jut of rubble and pointing shale.
             In the cracks of rocks grew brown Coreopsis,
             Blazing Star and False Mallow.
             With hard small centres like stones,
             Their dusty heads dragged against the scarce dirt;
             Their roots twisted among the pebbles of the butte —
             A mat of clinging fingers; their stalks, red
             And wiry, recoiled from the rising winds.
             For the surveyors it was a topographical
                elevation,
             Separating the three bitter lakes
             From the weed-green mud of sweet water
             In the fourth lake. It was a
             Feature of Townships 1 and 2, Range 19,
             West of the 2nd Meridian, an outcropping
             To defy their gridded mapping. It had no name,
(WIND   Indian or white. From the height of the cliffs,
FADES)   Southwards, the wide land rolls greyly
             Into the distance, strewn with heavy boulders,
             Smudged with salt flats and stale
             With the smoking lakes and the heavy
             Stink of rotting sulphur. There is no green
             Southwards. But northwards it was a hill
             To catch first sight of the watering hole,
             A peak of jubilation. No buffalo run,

No practical use, no mystery or magic,
A rise for prowling coyotes, nameless.

(NO SOUND EFFECTS DURING THE FOLLOWING LETTER)

BEAUBIER: Dear Sir:
(at "D")

BEAUBIER: I have the honour to acknowledge the receipt
(at "B")   of your letter dated August 23rd. I am being so
bold as to answer this letter in the stead of Mr.
Thomas Greenaway, Dominion Land Surveyor,
since he has been missing from our party some ten
days now and has not been seen. He left the main
camp to search out fresh water on the last day of
August as our supplies had become low, due to
breakage of three of the four barrels.

I am being so bold as to answer this letter in the stead of Mr.

A search party has been sent out — several
labourers, chainers, and the reckoning boy, who
is very much attached to the person of Mr.
Greenaway. The cook refused to go. We have
been taken to a spring by passing Indians.

I am proceeding with the surveying as per
original instructions, but you will appreciate, I
am sure, the tardiness in our progress due to the
absence of Mr. Greenaway.

I have the honour to be, Sir,
your obedient servant
Henri Beaubier,
Evening, September, 1910

(COULEE   Post Scriptum: This land is desert, not fit
SOUNDS)   for farming.

(THE COULEE SOUNDS COME UP AS LETTER ENDS. THEY INCLUDE SUCH
SOUNDS AS CONSTANT RUSTLING OF ASPEN GROVE, SINGING BIRDS, TWIGS
CRACK. NO WIND AS SUCH. IN BACKGROUND AN INDIAN SONG, PERHAPS A
LULLABY. THE COULEE SOUNDS CAN COME FROM ALL POINTS BUT SHOULD BE
CONCENTRATED AT "B")

NARRATOR: The coulees here are fissures in the ground;
(at "D") Edges slant down into the long, uncommon grass,
Brush of red roseflesh and honeysuckle, and at the
bottom,
Wet, with trees and lush, soft grasses,
The deer come to shed their spikes in the
Shadowed bottoms of the coulees. Weathered
deer-scat
By the bushes. The earth is soft.
Spongy, everything here leaves tracks.
Nothing passes unnoticed. Below the level of the
prairie
But high in the sky of the short coulee days,
The dead are buried in the treetops.
Night is close and eternal.
The mummied dead in the maples, the mummied
dead
In the aspens and birch, soughed in the air drafts,
Like cocoons, the bark ties frayed, disentangling.
The dead will settle into the lush grass.
Children are laid on the low shrubbery
Like small, wrapped mists of the dank coulee
morning,
And the trees are alive with the songs of birds.
Here, the prairie nomads camp;
The men, weary from the hunt,
Their women, bringing hot fires to the coulee
Bottom. When they come, the deer trembles
In the thicket and stands motionless
Over her fawns, while the moaning women
Bundle up their failed births for burial
And bundle their live ones for sleep.
In the encampment one woman's heart
Beat with the heartbeat of the deer;
Sightless, she listened to the thud of her own heart.

274 Where Is My Home?

She was among the women but the closeness
Of the doe tore her away from the women's talk,
And she trembled.

AYEE:　　He calls me Ayee,
(at "E")　　But my name is "the deer".
LULLABY　　I have hidden afraid
LOUDER　　In the coulee trees,
　　　　　I have trembled.

NARRATOR:　In the sweet air of a summer morning
(at "D")　　The deer anxiously struggle up the slopes,
　　　　　Through the brush of the coulee sides.
　　　　　Rusty thorns catch in their hide.

AYEE:　　I am torn
(at "E")　　By a tangle of roses.

NARRATOR:　They graze on the young spring grass,
(at "D")　　Lying on the prairie among the crocuses
PRAIRIE　　With their backs to the wind, chewing
WIND AT　　The new cud of succulent growth,
"E"　　　The winter scent of their faded grey coats
　　　　　Rises on the soft winds.

AYEE:　　There, on the prairie,
(at "E")　　He found me,
　　　　　The man who marks out
　　　　　The starpoints of the earth,
　　　　　Who measures the land
　　　　　With the long eye
　　　　　Of his instrument.
　　　　　He came at the sound of morning
　　　　　When the deer struggle
　　　　　Up from the coulee.
　　　　　And I went with him.

(SOUND OF WIND STRONGER. COULEE SOUNDS FADE OUT)

It is a year
I last heard birds
Quarrelling in the trees
A year since I found
In my breast
The deer's heart
And bounded away
From my people.
All winter I whispered
In his ear like a spring breeze,
And his heart bent.
First, he said,
I must chain the prairie,
Then, I will run with you,
My Ayee.
Now he is gone;
He left behind
The glass that sees
Everything near.
He is lost in the distance.

(WITH THE WIND ARE NOW HEARD THE SOUNDS OF MARSH BIRDS AND GULLS.
THE MARSH CALLS OF THESE BIRDS ARE EMPHASIZED)

NARRATOR: Willets walk, one or two together,
(at "B")   Along the salt-crusted stones of the water lines,
              Pecking disdainfully at the stinking
              Lakes, where only small brine shrimp breed.
              Amongst the gravel grow bright Samphire
              And Glasswort the color of water,
              Their small flowers embedded
              In bitter, juicy stems, their roots
              Weakly holding them to the brackish wetlands.
              The bowl of sky clamped tight to the bowl
              Of earth. Rocks heave out of the ground,
              Single clouds scrape close to the horizon.

Everything is sucked to the brackish centre
Of the world and the walking willets.
Not a feather out of place.

TOM: Salt again!
(at "A") Three lakes of stinking, putrid water
The fresh must be further south,
That ignorant, old devil didn't know how to make
    a map.
Look, he shows the sweet water two miles east
Of here, in the middle of that desert
I walked across this afternoon.
My bladder shrivelled in that terrible sun
And he found water? I can still feel
The burn of that cracked, grey earth
Through the soles of my boots.
Well Tom, maybe he saw the same
Lake and trees you did, floating
Two feet above the ground.
    Mirages!
Wish young Beaubier'd been with me —
I'd sent him off after it with a pail.
I should have brought more water.
Canteen's half empty already (PAUSE)
Tom, it's a stupid, bullheaded pride
You've got. Goin off lookin for water
At 56 years of age, when you could
Have sent that green horn Frenchie out.
He'd've carried along a bottle of his fancy brandy.
Don't begrudge him it, Tom,
He needs it to keep him warm at night.
I should have brought Ayee with me —
A woman keeps a man warm.
He wouldn't've even known how to make a fire
Out on the bald prairie. So what do you get, Tom,
For all your knowledge? A night in a blanket

On the ground that throws up the dead. No
    wonder
The Indians hang them up in the trees close to the
    sun.
That great butte there's not even on this map.
What use is a map like this? I'll use it
To light a fire to-night and might it
Add a little warmth to his old surveyor's soul
That's surely burning in hell. Ayee
Always says, This land don't want to be charted.
Well, Tom, nothing to do but head for that butte
And have us a look-see.
There's no rest for the wicked.

(THE SOUNDS OF SHORE BIRDS AND GULLS CEASE. WIND CONTINUES)

NARRATOR: On the abrupt sand face of the crag
(at "B")   Bank swallows have punched
           Nesting holes in the crumbling wall.
           They shoot out of the sheer face
           Of sand, flashing white breasts
           As small as heartbeats, strike
           Upward, turn in long parabolas of
           Soundlessness: hundreds of them,
           Knifing the blue.

(WIND FADES. NIGHT SOUNDS AT "A" AND "E")

AYEE: Why did the skyman
(at "D")   Go by himself?
           I felt his retreating footsteps
           Across the prairie,
           Heard him shout·out
           Something not for me.
           They said to get water.
           We do not need water.
           In two days it will rain.
           The air is troubled
           Tonight,

The air pulls at my feet
Like the wind
Of winter, scraping
The ground.
The callings of owls and coyotes
Resound like shadows over the stars,
I hear the movements
Of sleepless deer.
Even now my head is hot
From the fanged sun,
Oh, the man was a running stream
That could not be dammed.
I feel troubled tonight;

(WIND COMES UP. NIGHT SOUNDS CONTINUE)

TOM: Getting dark. Maybe I can see something
(at "A")   From the top. Better be careful.
           This time of year probably rattler young-uns
           around.

NARRATOR: The prairie rattlesnake is a timid reptile,
(at "B")   Light sandy, greenish or greyish brown,
           With dark brown patches on the back
           And small patches along the sides; it
           Passes unnoticed. But if aroused
           Or surprised, it rears and
           Its fangs flick out of hiding
           Places along the roof of the mouth
           And, guided by heat sensitive pits
           Between the nostril and eye on either side,
           It spears its warm-blooded enemy with unfailing
           Accuracy, even in total darkness.
           If you are careful where you walk
           And wear high boots, it is unlikely
           You will run afoul of the coiled buzz.
           But "there is no more foolish act
           When climbing in the badlands

Than placing one's hands on ledges
Without being first able to see
If they are inhabited. These are
Favourite rattlesnake resting places."

AYEE: I hear him call;
(at "D")   I must go to him,
           Leave silently, not wake
           The camp curs.
           I will follow
           The track of his voice
           On the night wind.

(HEAVY WIND AT "B" AND "D")

TOM: Men have survived snakebite. On the neck?
(at "C")   If I lie still, rest, let the warm venom
           Work itself out of my system.
           Well, Tom, you've got yourself
           In a fine mess. Go sticking your head
           In a snake's nest. You could have
           Tried the butte in the morning. In
           The morning, when you could have seen better.
           Snakes, I hear them moving over the hot stones
           In the dark. Their tongues flicking, flicking.
           Those old rattlers get a mite cranky, Tom,
           When you rub eyeballs with them.

AYEE: He's come this way.
(at "D")   What does he seek
           Of these lakes?
           These running sores?

TOM: I have water for another day — maybe
(at "C")   My throat! Getting hard to swallow.
           Oldtimers say no one ever need die of snakebite.

AYEE: Dryland, why
(at "D")   Do you lure him

To the poisoned waters
Seeping from your core?

NARRATOR: Venoms are proteins related to the albumen
(at "E")   In the white of an egg. They contain both toxic
                 And anti-toxic substances. Among the toxic,
                 A coagulin, a haemolysin, a haemhorragin and
                 A neurotoxin have been isolated.

TOM: All you have to do is kill the snake,
(at "C")   Cut out its liver and eat it.
                 That'll cure any bite.

NARRATOR: The coagulin
(at "E")   Is a diastase, which comes from the white
                 Blood corpuscles, and acts within the blood
                     vessels,
                 Inducing clots which may lead to death through
                 Embolism. Its action is transient since it is
                 Offset by that of the haemolysin, which breaks
                     down
                 The red corpuscles. Haemhorragin acts on the
                     walls
                 Of the capillaries, allowing blood to pass into
                 The tissues: especially of the skin, lungs
                 Intestines and bladder.

TOM: He stabbed me before I even seen him.
(at "C")

NARRATOR: Neurotoxin has a
(at "E")   Selective action on the nervous system. It acts
                 On the brain, bringing about stupor and
                 A dazed condition. By attacking the spinal cord,
                 It causes first, paralysis, and, after reaching the
                     medulla,
                 Nausea, sickness and profuse sweating.

BEAUBIER: Dear Sir;
(at "A")   I have the honour to acknowledge the receipt

of your letter dated September 19th. In the matter of Mr. Thomas Greenaway, I am grieved to advise you that I must file a report of his demise.

TOM:
(at "C")
(WIND RESUMES)

If you just lie here quiet, breathing slow.
There's your lake, Tom, to the north.
Two, three miles. And southwards, the salt lakes,
Steaming, smell the stink from here.
Water, have to drink. Have to drink. Just a little.
There! Still lots if I save it.
Ah, Ayee, bring me water in your brown hands;
Cup me in your cool hands like dew.

Tuesday

BEAUBIER:
(at "A")

last we captured an Indian who had in his possession Mr. Greenway's compass which said Indian carried in an ornate shoulderbag, which men in my company assure me is a medicine bag. It is therefore to be assumed that the prisoner attached some sort of superstitious value to the object in question. Subsequent to our discovery, we elicited a more complete account of his gaining possession of the compass.

He told an improbable tale of having seen several weeks ago at sunrise, a man dancing and writhing on top of a high butte north of three salt lakes. He took this dance to be one to placate the angry sky god. For at that time, an electrical storm encircled the hills of the valley and seemed to turn on the centre of the butte's height. He remarked on the unusual time, early morning, of this phenomenon. And it is true that such violent storms usually come in the evening, as an aftermath of the building up of heat in the valley during the day.

TOM:
(at "C")

Ducks fly over without stopping.
Nothing, nothing finds me here. Tom,

What's the matter with you? They know
Where you've gone. Tomorrow night
They'll organize a search party.
Wind here on the butte strong, no cover.
Tomorrow, sun. If I could sleep!
My tongue swells to choke me, choke off
Sleep. Nothing sleeps here, everything is still,
Nothing sleeps.

AYEE: It is a year
(at "D") He has stridden before me.
He bound the wild land
With his steel thongs.
Now, I feel a weariness
In his steps.
The earth is slowing
Him, his feet drag
In the heat of the land.
He kicks the dirt
And grey dust rises
To choke him. He tramples
The rocks, they turn
And strike him
With their teeth of stone.
Why did he follow
The stink of the bitter lakes?
Why did he not go north
To the watering hole?
The earth pulls him down
To her sour caves.
There are fresh water lakes,
Treed coulees, where he
Could find water.
But the earth hides them from him.
I feel him move;
He turns in his sleep
But cannot sleep

BEAUBIER: Subsequent to obtaining this information, I
(at "A")   organized yet another search party of six men
              including myself, the Indian and the boy, who was
              so close to Mr. Greenaway and who would not be
              left behind. On arriving at the butte, the Indian
              pointed to a cairn of rocks at the top, but refused
              to make the ascent with us. The boy, two others
              and myself climbed to the peak. The rocks were
              piled pyramidically with some care at the highest
              point of the butte, from which place we gained a
              panoramic view of the entire countryside.

NARRATOR: The symptoms of rattlesnake poisoning
(at "E")   Are as follows: the painful wound
(WIND   Is speedily discouloured and swollen.
LIGHT)   As a rule, constitutional symptoms appear
              In less that fifteen minutes.
              Prostration, staggering, cold sweats, vomiting,
              Feeble and quick pulse, dilation of the pupil,
              And slight mental disturbance. In this state
              The patient may die in about twelve hours.

BEAUBIER: Against the cairn, we found Mr. Greenaway's
              canteen, binoculars and rifle. At the bottom, and
              about six inches from the ground, was a flat,
              projecting rock. On this ledge, we discovered Mr.
              Greenaway's sidereal watch. I am bound to report
              that the watch was still running. I am at a loss to
              explain how this could be since it has been now
              over a month since Mr. Greenaway left camp —
              excepting that someone has regularly wound it.

TOM: All night I hear the movement
(at "C')   Of animals; they come close, they wait,
(WIND   They breathe the frosted air,
RESUMES)   They creep out from the shadow of boulders,
              Along the ridges of the peeled earth's surface,

Shifting their weight in the spiked grass,
Watching me from black eyes, stopping
Me from sleep. Watching . . .

AYEE: His body is blinded:
(at "D")   The sickness of my eyes.

BEAUBIER: This I believe to be the case.
(at "A")   I decided that it was inadvisable at this late date
                 to disturb the remains, and so I returned to camp.
                 I am packing and shipping to the Department the
                 effects of Mr. Greenaway, excluding the following
                 items, which I am retaining to complete the
                 survey:
                        one sidereal watch
                        one transit theodolite (Keuffel and Esser)
                        one aneroid barometer
                        one clinometer
                        one 100 foot steel band chain
                 If it is agreeable to the Department, I shall
                 proceed with Contract No. 23 of Mr. Greenaway
                 and expect to complete the work by the end of
                 October.
                              I have the honour to be, Sir,
                              your obedient servant
                              Henri Beaubier
                              October 2, 1910

Dear Sir:
        Pursuant to my letter of October 2, I beg to
        report that further questioning of the Indian by
        the Mounted Police revealed that Mr. Green-
        away's death was occasioned by a self-inflicted
        and mortal wound.

TOM: (Groaning) my head aches with dark lucifer's
(at "D")   night
                 beasts prowling crawling breathing on me

Wild Man's Butte   285

ECHOES *echoes* echoes light dims the stars my
hand swollen black dirt on the rim of the valley
hands thick as necks fingers strangle the sun with
black ropes brass sun suns suns a circle of
cold suns god have mercy on me the wind blows
    me
my feet far away down on the earth far below me
my feet move far above me my voice cries out I
call to you. Sun, hear me sun's in my head Ayee
your smoky eyes your slow grey tears

BEAUBIER: It is claimed by the prisoner that he and
(at "A")   several other Indians saw Mr. Greenaway, astride the butte, place a rifle to his head and pull
the trigger.

TOM: get away from
(at "E")   me they're crawling over my body where's my rifle
up up oh god I can feel them on my legs around
    my
chest can't breathe stand up my rifle up there
go away get off they're tightening can't breathe
off off they're trying to kill me I can feel them
inside my gut in my gut the sun is spilling snakes
    into
the sky over top of me my shells where's my
shells one-two-three uh, four five that'll do
it Tom I'll shoot them off the sun BAM BAM
    BAM
too many of them Bam I can't get them all they're
inside me in my head coiling in my skull
Aaaaaarghhhh tightening they're swallowing my
    eyes BAM

(LONG, ECHOING SHOT, FADING AWAY LIKE THUNDER. SILENCE THEN WIND
FAINTLY HEARD AND THE CALLS OF SWALLOWS)

NARRATOR: Against the dawn, at the rounded
(at "C")   Edges of the sand cliffs, snakes

Slide out and over, down
The face, flicking their tongues, scenting
The warm staleness of mothered nests.

BEAUBIER:
(at "A")

This story seems to me a shameless prevarication, designed, in all likelihood, to conceal some crime that might be attributed to the prisoner if the body were exhumed. Mr. Greenaway's character was not such that he would have chosen this ignominious end. Nor do I know of any cause in his life immediately before the unfortunate events which would have led him to choose such an unnatural demise.

NARRATOR:
(at "C")

The brown-spotted eggs of the swallow left
By terrified birds, that screech
In the wind, swooping at the stretched,
Sucking lengths of reptile. The snakes
Swallow the eggs whole and withdraw.

BEAUBIER:
(at "A")

Also I should like to report in strictest confidence to shield the sensibilities of Mr. Greenaway's immediate family, that while in the field, and during the past winter, when he did not return East as was his wont, he had taken to himself a young Indian woman.

(INDIAN MOURNING SONG BEGINS VERY FAINTLY. RISES TO A CLIMAX DURING TOM'S LAST SPEECH)

I am sure that she meant very little to him, the needs of the flesh sometimes outweighing the more civilized principles of social behaviour. But she did leave camp two days after Mr. Greenaway set out, which I thought strange at the time, seeing that he was due back in camp that evening. I do not wish to suggest that she was in anyway implicated, but the coincidence of her departure, just before the presumed time of his death makes it encumbent upon me to report this information for your consideration. Mr. Greenaway did not mention her name or treaty number to me, nor can I find them amongst his papers. I am, therefore, at a loss to know how she might be traced, if the Department desires to do so. I might add that the young squaw was blind, although not totally so.

> I have the honour to be, Sir,
> your obedient servant,
> Henri Beaubier
> October 3, 1910

> Post Scriptum: The Indian claims that the body was black colour when they reached it.

TOM:
(at "E")

Crusts of blood, dark streams . . .
A deer comes to me in the waves of heat,
Hooves moving over the salt matted sand.
I wipe her away from my eyes but always
There, the same, floating over the flatland
To this butte. Am I dreaming
A last time? Tom,
You could have blasted away the half of
Your head that didn't do the dreaming.
The deer comes, her pelt is tanned
And beaded like the garments of my Ayee.
Poor, blind doe,
Picking her way up this cliff,
Searching between darkness and light,
Staring through the grey milk of her eyes,
She comes so slowly, drops
Of her blood smear on the rocks.
Ayee? Is it you?
Have they hurt you
In the monthly cycle of the hunted?

Your sewn pelt is dry and grey, turning
To dust. By the time you reach
Me, you'll have powdered
And blown across the spikards of grass.
But your blood is still bright and red,
Like water.

(WIND RISING, LIGHT THUNDER, THEN RAIN)

AYEE:
(at "C")
My hunter, warrior
Star man.
I was coming.
I heard the thunder
Of your weapon from the hill.
From across the valley
I heard you fall
Like a wounded beast.

You have brought the sky
Down with you.
The sun trembles
In the black clouds;
The earth rumbles.
It is the beginning
Of the day.

Who has killed this?

I touch your head,
Blood, dust,
A stillbirth
Wrenched from my womb.

Who has killed this one?

Sun? Morning wind? Earth?
Earth.
Dear Sir:
    I have the honour to acknowledge the receipt
of your letter dated October 20th. This is to in-

form you of our discontinuance of the surveying of Range 220 for this season. The unusually early cold and snow have prevented us from completing the contract, and I send herewith the last Progress Report for Subdivision Survey made under Contract No. 23 of 1910. I took the occasion of our returning in the vicinity to visit the cairn and last resting place of Dominion Land Surveyor, Thomas Greenaway. The peak of the butte was bitterly cold and I only stayed a few moments. I regret it was not possible to have his earthly remains shipped East where he might have had a decent burial by those who loved him. Upon my return, I shall most certainly carry my condolences to his wife and children.

The deer are suprisingly plentiful this autumn and we have enjoyed a good supply of meat from this source for the past two months.

> I continue to be, Sir,
> your obedient servant,
> Henri Beaubier
> Late Afternoon,
> November 2nd, 1910

NARRATOR: September is rutting time.
(at "C")   The drylands are cooled by the rains of autumn.
(RAIN)   Now, under the trees of the coulee, the bucks stamp
Out their territories and fight for chosen place,
Antler against antler, they bellow in to the cooling air.
Under the yellowing leaves, they bellow
In the evening, stamping the ground.
The doe comes from the dew of the morning,
Lifting her feet, sniffs at the stamped
And straggled grass blades, feeling
The heat in her white haunches,

Answers the buck with a gentle bleat.
There, on the stamped field, she lies down
And waits. Together they will find a place
Near water.

AYEE: He called me Ayee
(at "C")   My name is "the deer".

NARRATOR: In the dark of the coulee,
(at "C")   The days are short,
            Curled in the grass, the doe
            Is content to be with her mate
            At this end of the year.

AYEE: The rains of autumn
(at "C")   Are cold.

NARRATOR: Long ago, the people of the coulee moved
(at "C")   To another valley. A place marked out for them,
            They left their dead in the trees.

(RAIN BECOMES STEADY DOWNPOUR, CONTINUES TO END)

AYEE: Between two thin poplars
(at"C")   In a swaddle of soft skins,
            In a sling of bark,
            I have hung him,
            close to the stars
            With his face uncovered.
            He looks straight at the sky,
            Scans it with his eyes,
            With his salt water eyes.

            I guard him all day
            From crows; all night,
            from the whirr of owls,
            He looks forever
            Into the heavens,
            Forever he watches the sky.

(SILENCE)

NARRATOR: And, another time, the woman said
(at "C")

WOMAN: To the man: "My fire has gone out.
(at "A") You are a son of the sky. Go up there
And bring me a star."
But man sat, bent, huddled
To the earth, clutching his cloak of warm skins

MAN: Close to him. "Woman," he said, "I have grown
old
(at "E") And blind. I cannot see the sky."

Acknowledgements

The editor wishes to thank the authors and publishers for permission to include the following in this anthology:

R. Blake Allan for "Indian Woman" by Frederick Niven from *Stories from Western Canada.*

Ed Arrol "The Chinese Café".

D. P. Barnhouse for "The Pinch Hitters".

The Book Society of Canada Limited for "So Young, So Brave" by Clive Lytle from *First Flowering,* copyright 1956 by Anthony Frisch.

Elizabeth Brewster for "The Night Grandma Died" from *Passage of Summer* (Ryerson, 1969).

Sheryl Brown for "The Last Rose" from *Jasper Place Composite High School Literary Magazine.*

Gordon Burles for "She Goes Away".

Mary Jo Burles for "Carpet of Roses" from *Chinook Arch.*

Delphine Burrell for "Early Emigrant" from the *Alberta Poetry Yearbook.*

Canadian Authors Association for "Heritage" by Magda Rice and "Teddy at Kispiox Village" by Michael G. Coleman from *Spirit of Canada.*

The Canadian Publishers, McClelland and Stewart Limited for "The Outlaw" and "Cornet at Night" by Sinclair Ross from *The Lamp at Noon and Other Stories.* For "Petite Misère" by Gabrielle Roy from *Street of Riches.* For "Scrapbook" by Rudy Wiebe from *Where is the Voice Coming From?* For "To Set Our House In Order" by Margaret Laurence. For "Each Mountain" and "The Prairie" by Sid Marty from *Headwaters.* For "Buffalo Lake" by Ella Elizabeth Clark from *Indian Legends of Canada.*

Clarke Irwin & Company Limited for "Sleep" by Emily Carr from *Klee Wyck,* copyright 1951.

Doubleday & Co. Inc. for "Jewish Christmas" by Fredelle Bruser Maynard from *Raisins and Almonds.*

Denise Fair for "Legacy Defaulted" from *Totem.*

Marya Fiamengo for "British Columbia Gothic" from *Skookum Wawa.*

John Patrick Gillese for "Kirby's Gander".

House of Anansi Press Limited for "120 Miles North of Winnipeg" by Dale Zieroth from *12 Prairie Poets.*

Hudson's Bay Publishing for "Potlatch in the Park" by James K. Nesbitt from *The Beaver,* March 1954.

Terrence Heath and Anne Szumigalski for "Wild Man's Butte".

Hurtig Publishers for "Lost at Sea" by Maurice Metayer from *Tales from the Igloo.*

I-Syin for "My Home, My Home" from *Heritage* magazine.

Dorothy Livesay for "Canadiana" from *39 Degrees Below: The Anthology of Greater Edmonton Poetry.*

Macmillan Company of Canada Ltd. for "Fog" by Ethel Wilson from *The Urban Experience.* For "Anemone" by Dorothy M. Powell from *Singing Under Ice.*

Miriam Mandel for "Moose Jaw, Saskatchewan".

Beverley Mitchell for "Letter from Sakaye" from *Skookum Wawa.*

Oberon Press for "The Burning" by W. D. Valgardson from *Bloodflowers.* For "Larksong" by W. P. Kinsella from *Dance Me Outside.*

Oxford University Press for "Provincial" and "Transformations" by Miriam Waddington from *Driving Home.*

Gwen Pharis Ringwood for "Some People's Grandfathers" from *Stories from Across Canada.*

Kathy Roberts for "Elegy For My Family".

George Salverson Jr. for "A Visit to the Immigrant Sheds" by Laura Goodman Salverson from *Confessions of an Immigrant's Daughter.*

Barry Stevens for "Grade Five Geography Lesson" from *Number One Northern*.
Bill van Veelen for "The Fall Sun".
David Waltner-Toews for "Tante Tina's Lament" from *Number One Northern*.
Norman Ward for "Burns Night".

While every effort has been made to trace the owners of copyrighted material and to make due acknowledgment, we regret having been unsuccessful with the following selections:

"Making A Sale" by Evans Thordarson
"A Mouthful of Tongue" by Adele Wiseman
"My Grandfather" by Richard Chief Calf
"Region and Heritage" by Maara Haas
"in/dian" by Skyros Bruce
"On Being Canadian" by Michael Luchkovich
"The Kiskatinaw Songs" by Sean Virgo and Susan Musgrave from *Heritage*
"Gregg Cabin" by Jody McCurdy
"I Remember" by Terri Kishkan
"Damian" by Amy Marie George